JACK D. DOUGLAS

is Associate Professor of Sociology,
University of California, San Diego.

He has written extensively on
the major threats to our society—
technology, suicide, pollution.

THE TECHNOLOGICAL THREAT

Edited by
JACK D. DOUGLAS

A SPECTRUM BOOK

Prentice-Hall, Inc., *Englewood Cliffs, New Jersey*

C–13–902189–2
P–13–902171–X

Library of Congress Catalog Card Number 76–140275

Printed in the United States of America

Current printing (last number): 10 9 8 7 6 5 4 3 2 1

Prentice-Hall International, Inc. (*London*)
Prentice-Hall of Australia, Pty. Ltd. (*Sydney*)
Prentice-Hall of Canada, Ltd. (*Toronto*)
Prentice-Hall of India Private Limited (*New Delhi*)
Prentice-Hall of Japan, Inc. (*Tokyo*)

301.15: 621-52

CONTENTS

Introduction / *Jack D. Douglas*   1

1 / AMERICAN SOCIETY AS A TECHNOLOGICAL SOCIETY   *5*

Notes on the Post-Industrial Society / *Daniel Bell*   8

The Technological Society / *Irene Taviss*   21

2 / THE IMPACT OF TECHNOLOGY ON AMERICAN VALUES   *37*

The Impact of Technology on Ethical Decision-Making / *Robert Nisbet*   39

The Crisis in Valuation / *Karl Mannheim*   55

3 / THE IMPACT OF THE ELECTRONICS REVOLUTION   *69*

Leisure and Work in Postindustrial Society / *David Riesman*   71

Some Moral and Technical Consequences of Automation / *Norbert Wiener*   92

v

4 / THE THREATS OF ALIENATION AND
SOCIAL TECHNOLOGY 103

The Disjunction of Culture and Social Structure /
Daniel Bell 107

Some Issues Concerning the Control of Human Behavior /
Carl R. Rogers and B. F. Skinner 122

5 / THE IMPACT OF TECHNOLOGY ON
POLITICAL VALUES 151

Liberal Values in the Modern World / C. Wright Mills
154

The Need for a New Political Theory / Lawrence K. Frank
162

Politics and Technology / Edward T. Chase 170

Jack D. Douglas

INTRODUCTION

Americans have long been aware of the fundamental ways in which technology produces basic changes in the external forms of our everyday lives. Older generations are most aware of this, since they have seen American society transformed from a predominantly agricultural society of small towns into a technological society of massive megalopolises. Many have seen the world transformed from the horse and buggy age into the jet and rocket age, from the age of kerosene lamps into the age of atomic power, from an age of epidemics into the age of antibiotics. But the young are also aware of the ways in which technology changes and rechanges their own clothes, houses, transportation, and entertainment.

We have long been accustomed to the eulogies on technology with which each new product and mode of production has been introduced. And most of us until recently looked only upon the benevolent aspects of technology, the labor-saving devices, the wealth-increasing modes of production, the life-saving "miracle drugs," and the greatly increased variety of products and entertainments. Indeed, it is likely that most Americans until quite recently vaguely expected that the scientific and technological revolution sweeping our society would someday soon carry us all into a *technological utopia* in which everyone would be wealthy, in which everyone would have unlimited leisure to spend his wealth, and, just possibly, in which no one would die.

The sudden realization of the threats to our natural environment from the multifarious forms of pollution, all of which stem directly or indirectly from the advance of technology, have put an end to these bright dreams of technological utopias. Rather than utopias, most

1

Americans today seem to fear that technology will soon produce an *environmental apocalypse*. Rather than eulogies on the bright hopes of the technological society, we now hear incessant warnings of impending doom.

The more extreme of these warnings of doom are undoubtedly overdrawn. They seem to be largely the emotional excesses of our general anxieties over the rise of the technological society, a totally new kind of human society in which science and technology dictate the dominant forms of thought and increasingly shape almost every aspect of our everyday lives. Still, there is little doubt that even the most sober analysis of our technologically induced environmental problems must lead to the conclusion that these problems are very severe and will be difficult and costly to remedy. If they do not lead to an irrational scattering of our efforts, these anxious excesses in our concerns with the environmental threats of technology could even prove helpful by leading to the public commitment to solve them that has so long been needed.

But there is a serious danger that this anxious concern with the physical effects of the technological revolution might prevent our seeing potentially far more serious social problems arising from this revolution. For there are far deeper potential threats arising from this revolution than those that can so easily be seen or felt. Because technology increasingly shapes almost every realm of our everyday lives, and through formal education has increasingly become the dominant form of modern thought, it could transform or destroy the social foundations of our most cherished human values.

Those who look at human life only from an idealistic perspective, or assume man is absolutely free to choose whatever he wishes in his life, often look at values as totally independent of the practical realities of everyday life and as the sole causes of the patterns of our everyday lives. But, however satisfying these assertions may be to some of us, there is no support for them in the knowledge of human society we have gained from the social sciences. While the social sciences have too often gone to the opposite extreme of denying all freedom to human beings, our studies have always shown that human beings are not able to totally abstract themselves from the practical situations in which they find themselves and impose their values completely on their practical situations. Instead, we find that the practical realities of our everyday lives *interact* with our values and the other meanings we give to our lives; our values, ideas, beliefs and feelings do help to shape the external forms of our lives, and we do have some degree of freedom in choosing how they are to do this; but, at the same time, the external, practical realities of our everyday lives eventually have great effects on our values, ideas, beliefs and feelings. A determined people may maintain their most cherished values for long periods of time, even against basic changes in their external forms of life that once sup- ported and fit their values, but eventually the practical situations they face do change their values. Indeed, the slowness with which the trans- formation in values takes place may simply help to prevent their be- coming aware of what is happening, an awareness which might lead them to try to prevent the external changes that are making their values impractical.

America is a highly pluralistic society and there are vast differences in the values of the different groups that make up our society. But there are also certain basic values shared by almost all the groups. These are especially the values on individual freedom, the integrity of the individual human life, and creative work leading to human progress and happiness. We also share values and ideas of democratic forms of government which embody these more basic values.

These fundamental values did not just appear on the historic scene, nor were they manufactured in the perfervid imaginations of some mythical Founding Fathers. There have certainly been many men over the centuries who believed in these values and sought to mold society on the basis of them because their reason and free imagination led them to believe that all men would be better off in a society dominated by such values. Some men were no doubt led to these values and ideas by their interpretations of Judeo-Christian traditions; others were led to them by their knowledge of democratic life in Ancient Athens; and still others were probably led to them by the peculiar practical circum- stances in which they found themselves. There were even some such men in the most tyrannical of ages, when the practical constraints of everyday life, and the choices of men of power who sought to main- tain their own privileges, made the success of such efforts impossible. But these values and ideas, and all the efforts and sacrifices of such men, did not triumph by becoming embodied or concretized in the external forms of everyday life until the practical constraints had changed.

Our most cherished values and our democratic forms of government became dominant in our Western societies partly through the creative efforts of men and largely through the growth of pluralism and the decentralization of power. Beginning vaguely with the pluralism and decentralization of power of feudal society, growing rapidly with the rise of a massive middle class, and reaching their zenith in the highly pluralistic and decentralized American frontier, these values on freedom and individualism and these forms of government have always flourished where there is pluralism and decentralization. *The technological society flourishes on homogeneity and centralization.* American democracy was built by men who were predominantly small farmers and merchants who lived and worked relatively independently of others. Technological America is a society of massive organizations in which all of us are highly dependent on all the rest of our society for our livelihoods.

No society, other than those conquered or destroyed from without, has ever experienced a more rapid and total transformation in its external, practical forms of life than American society has in the past century. Most of us have little doubt that many of these changes have been beneficial and most of us probably hope we can find ways to increase these benefits through further developments of science and technology. But a growing proportion of us has become aware of the ways in which some of these changes pose terrible threats to our cherished values of freedom and individualism and to our democratic forms of government. The purpose of this volume is to examine the bases for these threats in technology and the primary forms that these threats take. It is only by such systematic, critical examinations of the relations between the development of this massive technological society and our fundamental values and forms of government that we can hope to affect wise and free choices in policies that will prevent the destruction of those values and that form of government.

As the reader will readily perceive, the volume begins in Part 1 with a consideration of the nature of the transformation that has taken place and of the basic questions we must answer before we can make wise decisions on what to do in the years ahead. It then examines in Part 2 the ways in which technology affects our values. The succeeding Parts of the volume examine the potential threats of technology to our fundamental values and the kinds of things we can do to prevent these threats from destroying those values and forms of government.

There are no easy or final answers to the anguished questions we must face and answer in the years ahead. But surely there is hope that we may find sufficiently wise answers, however tentative, if we begin our search while there is still time to prevent the rise of a *technological tyranny.* I hope this volume will stimulate many others to take part in this search.

1 / AMERICAN SOCIETY
AS A TECHNOLOGICAL SOCIETY

Every society in the world is being profoundly affected by the scientific and technological revolution that started in Western societies approximately 500 years ago. In a very real sense, world society is being transformed by this scientific and technological revolution. Where we are heading and where we will wind up are very uncertain. Only the fact of change and its sources in the development of new scientific and technological knowledge are certain.

American society is at the very center of this world transformation and is the primary source of that transformation. It is American society that is being most rapidly and thoroughly changed by the revolution in scientific and technological knowledge.

We have now moved beyond the industrial society and into what Daniel Bell calls the *postindustrial society,* but which is also commonly called the technological society. The postindustrial society is of such recent origin, however unclearly it may be demarcated from the industrial society, that Daniel Bell believes it appropriate to set the symbolic beginning of the postindustrial society in 1956, when white-collar workers outnumbered blue-collar workers in our society for the first time. The postindustrial society is above all a society in which most individuals are freed from industrial production. Instead of working on assembly lines and at other kinds of preindustrial and industrial tasks, they do work which relies very heavily on a great deal of special knowledge and skill, either in creating or manning production facilities or in working with other human beings. But, as Bell so strongly emphasizes, it is not the dependence on knowledge alone which makes the postindustrial society so distinct; rather, it is the dependence on knowledge with the specific characteristic of being *theo-*

retical knowledge. Theoretical knowledge is knowledge that is abstracted from specific, concrete situations and can be applied to many new situations. It is this kind of knowledge which, in fact, is crucial to the development of new kinds of knowledge, or innovations. As Bell argues, every society now lives by innovation. And, since theoretical knowledge is the basis of innovation, theoretical knowledge becomes crucial to the life of every society, especially to American society. It follows, then, that since the university has become the center of theoretical knowledge in our society, the university has also become the center, or wellspring, of our society. Undoubtedly, this has been an important factor leading to the great struggles over the control of the university in recent years.

But as Bell also emphasizes, the centrality of theoretical knowledge to decision-making in our society today does not mean that knowledge alone determines the nature of the decision. In fact, he argues very persuasively that knowledge only becomes the condition for decision-making, not the determinant. Rather, decision-making for our society as a whole must still be effected through political processes. Political processes sometimes do not take knowledge into consideration to any significant degree. Usually, politicians make the decisions determining which knowledge is relevant and how it is to be applied in making the decisions. In this sense, the politicians remain dominant over the technocrats who provide the knowledge the politicians make use of.

Nevertheless, it is quite clear that the increasing reliance on theoretical knowledge for political decision-making has led to some basic changes in such decision-making in our society. Most importantly, there has been a slow but steady development in the direction of increasingly centralized planning of our political decisions. It is this which Irene Taviss examines in detail. Above all, she is concerned with the implications of this technologically induced reliance on social planning for American values. Secondly, she is concerned with the implications of these changes for the kinds of studies social scientists should be doing of our society. In an increasingly planned society, social scientists have become ever more crucial in political decision-making, as they alone can provide the kinds of scientific theoretical knowledge needed by political leaders to make effective decisions. But this raises many problems for the nature of the social sciences themselves which Taviss has examined.

This first part of our volume is, then, concerned with the basic properties of the technological society that is now rising in America and with the fundamental questions which all of us, but especially students of the social sciences, must ask ourselves and for which we must seek wise answers in the years ahead. Part 2 will then examine what the fundamental properties of values and technology are that produce the threats of technology for our fundamental values. That is, part 2 will show us why it is that the rise of technological America poses such threats to our values.

Daniel Bell

NOTES ON THE
POST-INDUSTRIAL SOCIETY

Speeding-up the Time Machine

It was once exceedingly rare to be able to observe the formation of institutions *de novo*. Social change was crescive and moved slowly. Adaptations were piecemeal and contradictory, the process of diffusion halting. In his reflections on history, thirty-five years ago, Paul Valéry, the quintessential French man of letters, remarked that:

> "There is nothing easier than to point out the absence, from history books, of major phenomena which were imperceptible owing to the slowness of their evolution. They escape the historian's notice because no document expressly mentions them. . . .
> "An event which takes shape over a century will not be found in any document or collection of memoirs. . . ."

Today, not only are we aware of, and trying to identify, processes of change, even when they cannot be "dated," but there has been a speeding-up of the "time machine," so that the interval between the initial impetus to change and its realization has been radically reduced. A study by Frank Lynn of twenty major technological innovations that have had a substantial economic and/or social impact during the last sixty to seventy years indicates that every step in the process of technological development and diffusion has accelerated during this period. Specifically:

"Notes on the Post-Industrial Society" by Daniel Bell. From The Public Interest *(1967): 24–35. Copyright National Affairs, Inc., 1967. Reprinted by permission of National Affairs, Inc.*

¶The average time span between the initial discovery of a new technological innovation and the recognition of its commercial potential decreased from 30 years (for technological innovations introduced during the early part of this century, 1880–1919) to 16 years (for innovations introduced during the post-World War I period) to 9 years (for the post-World War II period).

¶The time required to translate a basic technical discovery into a commercial product or process decreased from 7 to 5 years during the 60–70-year time period investigated.

¶The rate of diffusion (measured by economic growth) for technological innovations introduced during the post-World War II period was approximately *twice* the rate for post-World War I innovations and *four* times the rate for innovations introduced during the early part of this century.

Perhaps the most important social change of our time is the emergence of a process of direct and deliberate contrivance of change itself. Men now seek to anticipate change, measure the course of its direction and its impact, control it, and even shape it for predetermined ends.

The Prophet from the Past

More than a hundred and fifty years ago, the wildly brilliant, almost monomaniacal technocrat, Claude-Henri de Rouvroy, le Comte de Saint-Simon ("the last gentleman and the first socialist" of France), popularized the word *industrialism* to designate the emergent society, wherein wealth would be created by mechanized production rather than be seized through plunder and war. Past society, said Saint-Simon, had been military society, in which the dominant figures were noblemen, soldiers, and priests, and the leading positions in the society were based either on control of the means of violence or on the manipulation of religious myth. In the new society, the "natural élite" that would organize society in a rational, "positive" fashion would be the industrialists (actually the engineers or technocrats), for the methods of industry were methods of order, precision, and certainty, rather than of metaphysical thought. In this society, ordered by function and capacity, "the real noblemen would be industrial chiefs and the real priests would be scientists."

The revolution which ended feudal society—the French Revolution —could have ushered in the industrial society, said Saint-Simon, but it did not do so because it had been captured by metaphysicians, lawyers, and sophists, men with a predilection for abstract slogans. What was needed, Saint-Simon added, was a breed of "new men"—engineers, builders, planners—who would provide the necessary leadership. And since such leaders require some inspiration, Saint-Simon, shortly before his death, commissioned Rouget de l'Isle, the composer of the "Marseillaise," to write a new "Industrial Marseillaise." This "Chant des Industriels," as it was called, was given its première in 1821 before Saint-Simon and his friend Ternaus, the textile manufacturer, at the opening of a new textile factory in Saint-Ouen.

The episode takes on a somewhat comic air, especially when we read that a number of the Count's followers established a new religious cult of Saint-Simonianism to canonize his teachings. (In the monastic castle to which the followers of Saint-Simon retreated, garments were buttoned down the back so that, in socialist fashion, each man would require the help of another in order to dress.) And yet many of these same followers of Saint-Simon were also the men who, in the middle of the 19th century, redrew the industrial map of Europe.[1]

We may at this point leave the story of Saint-Simon and his followers to the *curiosa* of the history of ideas. But if, with the spirit rather than the method of Saint-Simon, one speculates on the shape of society forty or fifty years from now, it becomes clear that the "old" industrial order is passing and that a "new society" is indeed in the making. To speak rashly: if the dominant figures of the past hundred years have been the entrepreneur, the businessman, and the industrial executive, the "new men" are the scientists, the mathematicians, the economists, and the engineers of the new computer technology. And the dominant institutions of the new society—in the sense that they will provide the most creative challenges and enlist the richest talents—will be the intellectual institutions. The leadership of the new society will rest, not with businessmen or corporations as we know them (for a good deal of production will have been routinized), but with the research corporation, the industrial laboratories, the experimental stations, and the

1. It is not too much to say, Professor F. H. Markham has written, "that the St. Simonians were the most important single force behind the great economic expansion of the second Empire, particularly in the development of banks and railways." Enfantin, the most bizarre of the St. Simonians, formed the society for planning the Suez Canal. The former St. Simonians constructed many of the European railways—in Austria, Russia, and Spain. The brothers Emile and Isaac Pereire, who promoted the first French railway from Paris to Saint-Germain, also founded the Crédit Mobilier, the first industrial investment bank in France, as well as the great shipping company, the Compagnie Générale Transatlantique which today sails the *Flandre* and the *France,* and which gave its first ships the names of St. Simonian followers, including the *Saint-Simon* (1,987 tons).

universities. In fact, the skeletal structure of the new society is already visible.

The Transformation of Society

We are now, one might say, in the first stages of a post-industrial society. A post-industrial society can be characterized in several ways. We can begin with the fact that ours is no longer primarily a manufacturing economy. The service sector (comprising trade; finance, insurance and real estate; personal, professional, business, and repair services; and general government) now accounts for more than half of the total employment and more than half of the gross national product. We are now, as Victor Fuchs pointed out in *The Public Interest*, No. 2, a "service economy"—i.e., the first nation in the history of the world in which more than half of the employed population is not involved in the production of food, clothing, houses, automobiles, and other tangible goods.

Or one can look at a society, not in terms of where people work, but of what kind of work they do—the occupational divisions. In a paper read to the Cambridge Reform Club in 1873, Alfred Marshall, the great figure of neo-classical economics, posed a question that was implicit in the title of his paper, "The Future of the Working Classes." "The question," he said, "is not whether all men will ultimately be equal—that they certainly will not be—but whether progress may not go on steadily, if slowly, till, by occupation at least, every man is a gentleman." And he answered his question thus: "I hold that it may, and that it will."

Marshall's criterion of a gentleman—in a broad, not in the traditional genteel, sense—was that heavy, excessive, and soul-destroying labor would vanish, and the worker would then begin to value education and leisure. Apart from any qualitative assessment of contemporary culture, it is clear that Marshall's question is well on the way to achieving the answer he predicted.

In one respect, 1956 may be taken as the symbolic turning point. For in that year—for the first time in American history, if not in the history of industrial civilization—the number of white-collar workers (professional, managerial, office and sales personnel) outnumbered the blue-collar workers (craftsmen, semi-skilled operatives, and laborers) in the occupational ranks of the American class structure. Since 1956 the ratio has been increasing: today white-collar workers outnumber the blue-collar workers by more than five to four.

Stated in these terms, the change is quite dramatic. Yet it is also somewhat deceptive, for until recently the overwhelming number of white-collar workers have been women, who held minor clerical or sales jobs; and in American society, as in most others, family status is still evaluated on the basis of the job that the man holds. But it is at this point, in the changing nature of the male labor force, that a status upheaval has been taking place. Where in 1900 only fifteen percent of American males wore white collars (and most of these were independent small businessmen), by 1940 the figure had risen to twenty-five percent, and by 1970, it is estimated, about forty percent of the male labor force, or about twenty million men, will be holding white-collar jobs. Out of this number, fourteen million will be in managerial, professional, or technical positions, and it is this group that forms the heart of the upper-middle-class in the United States.

What is most startling in these figures is the growth in professional and technical employment. In 1940, there were 3.9 million professional and technical persons in the society, making up 7.5% of the labor force; by 1962, the number had risen to 8 million, comprising 11.8% of the labor force; it is estimated that by 1975 there will be 12.4 million professional and technical persons, making up 14.2% of the labor force.

A New Principle

In identifying a new and emerging social system, however, it is not only in such portents as the move away from manufacturing (or the rise of "the new property" which Charles Reich has described) that one seeks to understand fundamental social change. It is in the defining characteristics that the nerves of a new system can be located. The ganglion of the post-industrial society is knowledge. But to put it this way is banal. Knowledge is at the basis of every society. But in the post-industrial society, what is crucial is not just a shift from property or political position to knowledge as the new base of power, but a change in the *character* of knowledge itself.

What has now become decisive for society is the new centrality of *theoretical* knowledge, the primacy of theory over empiricism, and the codification of knowledge into abstract systems of symbols that can be translated into many different and varied circumstances. Every society now lives by innovation and growth; and it is theoretical knowledge that has become the matrix of innovation.

One can see this, first, in the changing relations of science and technology, particularly in the matter of invention. In the 19th and early

20th centuries, the great inventions and the industries that derived from them—steel, electric light, telegraph, telephone, automobile— were the work of inspired and talented tinkerers, many of whom were indifferent to the fundamental laws which underlay their inventions. On the other hand, where principles and fundamental properties were discovered, the practical applications were made only decades later, largely by trial-and-error methods.

In one sense, chemistry is the first of the "modern" industries because its inventions—the chemically created synthetics—were based on theoretical knowledge of the properties of macromolecules, which were "manipulated" to achieve the planned production of new materials. At the start of World War I, hardly any of the generals of the Western Allies anticipated a long war, for they assumed that the effective naval blockade of the Central powers, thus cutting off their supply of Chilean nitrates, would bring Germany to her knees. But under the pressure of isolation, Germany harnessed all her available scientific energy and resources to solving this problem. The result—the development of synthetic ammonia by Bosch and Haber—was a turning point, not only in Germany's capacity for waging war, but also in the connection of science to technology.[2]

In a less direct but equally important way, the changing association of theory and empiricism is reflected in the management of economies. The rise of macro-economics and of governmental intervention in economic matters is possible because new codifications in economic theory allow governments, by direct planning, monetary or fiscal policy, to seek economic growth, to redirect the allocation of resources, to maintain balances between different sectors, and even, as in the case of Great Britain today, to effect a controlled recession, in an effort to shape the direction of the economy by conscious policy.

2. In *Modern Science and Modern Man*, James Bryant Conant, who, before becoming a distinguished educator, was a prominent chemist, tells the story that when the United States entered World War I, a representative of the American Chemical Society called on Newton D. Baker, then Secretary of War, and offered the services of the chemists to the government. He was thanked and asked to come back the next day—when he was told that the offer was unnecessary since the War Department already had a chemist! When President Wilson appointed a consulting board to assist the Navy, it was chaired by Thomas Edison, and this appointment was widely hailed for bringing the best brains of science to the solution of naval problems. The solitary physicist on the board owed his appointment to the fact that Edison, in choosing his fellow members, had said to President Wilson, "We might have one mathematical fellow in case we have to calculate something out." In fact, as R. T. Birge reports, during World War I there was no such classification as "physicist"; when the armed forces felt the need of one, which was only occasionally, he was hired as a chemist.

And, with the growing sophistication of computer-based simulation procedures—simulations of economic systems, of social behavior, of decision problems—we have the possibility, for the first time, of large-scale "controlled experiments" in the social sciences. These, in turn, will allow us to plot "alternative futures," thus greatly increasing the extent to which we can choose and control matters that affect our lives.

In all this, the university, which is the place where theoretical knowledge is sought, tested, and codified in a disinterested way, becomes the primary institution of the new society. Perhaps it is not too much to say that if the business firm was the key institution of the past hundred years, because of its role in organizing production for the mass creation of products, the university will become the central institution of the next hundred years because of its role as the new source of innovation and knowledge.

To say that the primary institutions of the new age will be intellectual is not to say that the majority of persons will be scientists, engineers, technicians, or intellectuals. The majority of individuals in contemporary society are not businessmen, yet one can say that this has been a "business civilization." The basic values of society have been focused on business institutions, the largest rewards have been found in business, and the strongest power has been held by the business community, although today that power is to some extent shared within the factory by the trade union, and regulated within the society by the political order. In the most general ways, however, the major decisions affecting the day-to-day life of the citizen—the kinds of work available, the location of plants, investment decisions on new products, the distribution of tax burdens, occupational mobility— have been made by business, and latterly by government, which gives major priority to the welfare of business.

To say that the major institutions of the new society will be intellectual is to say that production and business decisions will be subordinated to, or will derive from, other forces in society; that the crucial decisions regarding the growth of the economy and its balance will come from government, but they will be based on the government's sponsorship of research and development, of cost-effectiveness and cost-benefit analysis; that the making of decisions, because of the intricately linked nature of their consequences, will have an increasingly technical character. The husbanding of talent and the spread of educational and intellectual institutions will become a prime concern for the society; not only the best talents, but eventually the entire complex of social prestige and social status, will be rooted in the intellectual and scientific communities.

Things Ride Men

Saint-Simon, the "father" of technocracy, had a vision of the future society that made him a utopian in the eyes of Marx. Society would be a scientific-industrial association whose goal would be the highest productive effort to conquer nature and to achieve the greatest possible benefits for all. Men would become happy in their work, as producers, and would fill a place in accordance with their natural abilities. The ideal industrial society would by no means be classless, for individuals were unequal in ability and in capacity. But social divisions would follow actual abilities, as opposed to the artificial divisions of previous societies, and individuals would find happiness and liberty in working at the job to which they were best suited. With every man in his natural place, each would obey his superior spontaneously, as one obeyed one's doctor, for a superior was defined by a higher technical capacity. In the industrial society, there would be three major divisions of work, corresponding, in the naive yet almost persuasive psychology of Saint-Simon, to three major psychological types. The majority of men were of the motor-capacity type, and they would become the laborers of the industrial society; within this class, the best would become the production leaders and administrators of society. The second type was the rational one, and men of this capacity would become the scientists, discovering new knowledge and writing the laws that were to guide men. The third type was the sensory, and these men would be the artists and religious leaders. This last class, Saint-Simon believed, would bring a new religion of collective worship to the people that would overcome individual egoism. It was in work and in carnival that men would find satisfaction; and in this positivist utopia, society would move from the governing of men to the administration of things.

But in the evolution of technocratic thinking,[3] things began to

3. The word *technocracy* itself was first coined in 1919 by William Henry Smyth, an inventor and engineer in Berkeley, California, in three articles published in *Industrial Management* of February, March, and May in that year. These were reprinted in a pamphlet, and later included with nine more articles, written for the *Berkeley Gazette*, in a larger reprint. The word was taken over by Howard Scott, a one-time research director for the Industrial Workers of the World, and was popularized in 1933–34, when Technocracy flashed briefly as a social movement and a panacea for the depression. The word became associated with Scott, and through him with Thorstein Veblen, who, after writing *The Engineers and the Price System*, had been associated earlier with Scott in an educational venture at the New School

ride men. For Frederick W. Taylor, who—as the founder of scientific management—was perhaps most responsible for the translation of technocratic modes into the actual practices of industry, any notion of ends other than production and efficiency of output was almost nonexistent. Taylor believed strongly that "status must be based upon superior knowledge rather than nepotism and superior financial power," and in his idea of functional foremanship he asserted that influence and leadership should be based on technical competence rather than on any other skills. But in his view of work, man disappeared, and all that remained was "hands" and "things" arranged, on the basis of minute scientific examination, along the lines of a detailed division of labor wherein the smallest unit of motion and the smallest unit of time became the measure of a man's contribution to work.

In the technocratic mode, the ends have become simply efficiency and output. The technocratic mode has become established because it is the mode of efficiency—of production, of program, of "getting things done." For these reasons, the technocratic mode has spread in our society. But whether the technocrats themselves will become a dominant class, and in what ways the technocratic mode might be challenged are different questions.

Soldiers Ride Things

It was the root idea of Saint-Simon, August Comte, and Herbert Spencer, the 19th-century theorists of industrial society, that there was a radical opposition between the industrial and the military spirit. The one emphasized work, production, rationality; the other display, waste, and heroics. Out of technology, economizing, and investment would come productivity as the basis of an increasing wealth for all, rather than exploit and plunder as the means of seizing wealth from others. In ancient society, work was subordinated to war and the warrior ruled; in industrial society, the times would become pacific and the producer would rule.

The irony is that, while the economizing spirit—the deployment of limited resources to attain maximum results—has indeed spread

---

for Social Research. Interestingly, when the word became nationally popular through Scott, it was repudiated by Smyth, who claimed that Scott's use of the word fused *technology and autocrat,* "rule by technicians responsible to no one"; whereas his original word implied "the rule of the people made effective through the agency of their servants, the scientists and technicians."

throughout society, it has been war rather than peace that has been largely responsible for the acceptance of planning and technocratic modes in government.

Instead of peace, every industrial society has a *Wehrwirtschaft*, a "preparedness economy," or a mobilized society. A mobilized society is one in which the major resources of the country are concentrated on a relatively few specific objectives defined by the government. In these sectors, in effect, private needs are subordinated to social goals and the role of private decision is correspondingly reduced. The Soviet Union is a mobilized society *par excellence*. Most of the "new states," in their quest for modernization, have become mobilized: the basic resources of the society—capital and trained manpower— are geared to planned economic change.

In recent years, America has taken on the features of a mobilized polity in that one of the crucial scarce resources, that of "research and development"—and more specifically, the work of most of the scientists and engineers in research and development—is tied to the requirements of the military and of war preparedness. The United States has not done this by outright commandeering of talents, or by restricting the right of nongovernmental units to engage in R & D. But since R & D is always a risk, in that no immediate payoffs or profits are assured, and the costs of R & D have become astronomical, few institutions other than the government can underwrite such expenditures. And the government has been compelled to do so because of the extraordinary revolutions in the art of war that have occurred since 1945.

In one sense, as Herman Kahn has pointed out, military technology has supplanted the "mode of production," in Marx's use of the term, as a major determinant of social structure. Since the end of World War II there have been almost three total revolutions in military technology, with complete and across-the-board replacement of equipment, as older weapons systems were phased out without being used. Neither World War I nor World War II represented such complete breaks in continuity.

The source of these accelerated revolutions—changes in the character of atomic weapons, from manned bombers to missiles, from fixed missiles to roving missiles and from medium-range to intercontinental missiles—has been concentrated research and development, concerted planning for new systems of weaponry. And the technology of "custom-crafted" missile construction, as against bombers, was a chief element in changing the "production-mix" of the aerospace industry labor force, so much so that the Budget Bureau Report on

Defense Contracting (The David Bell Report of 1962) estimated that the ratio of engineers and scientists to production workers in the aerospace industry was roughly one-to-one.

In the Economic Report of the President, presented to Congress in January 1963, President Kennedy declared: "The defense, space and atomic energy activities of the country absorb about two-thirds of the trained people available for exploring our scientific and technical frontiers. . . . In the course of meeting scientific challenges so brilliantly, we have paid a price by sharply limiting the scarce scientific and engineering resources available to the civilian sectors of the American economy." By now, it is likely that President Kennedy's estimates are too low.

Who Holds Power?

Decisions are a matter of power, and the crucial questions in any society are: who holds power, and how is power held? Forty-five years ago, as we have noted, Thorstein Veblen foresaw a new society based on technical organization and industrial management, a "soviet of technicians," as he put it in the striking language he loved to employ in order to scare and mystify the academic world. In making this prediction, Veblen shared the illusion of Saint-Simon that the complexity of the industrial system and the indispensability of the technicians made military and political revolutions a thing of the past. "Revolutions in the 18th century," Veblen wrote, "were military and political; and the Elder Statesmen who now believe themselves to be making history still believe that revolutions can be made and unmade by the same ways and means in the 20th century. But any substantial or effectual overturn in the 20th century will necessarily be an industrial overturn; and by the same token, any 20th-century revolution can be combatted or neutralized only by industrial ways and means."

This syndicalist idea that revolution in the 20th century could only be an "industrial overturn" exemplifies the rationalist fallacy in so much of Veblen's thought. For, as we have learned, though technological and social processes are crescive, the crucial turning points in a society are political events. It is not the technocrat who ultimately holds power, but the politician.

The major changes which have reshaped American society over the past thirty years—the creation of a managed economy, a welfare society, and a mobilized polity—grew out of political responses: in

the first instances to accommodate the demands of economically inse-
cure and disadvantaged groups—the farmers, workers, Negroes, and
the poor—for protection against the hazards of the market; and,
later, as a consequence of the concentration of resources and political
objectives following the mobilized postures of the Cold War and the
space race.

The result of all this is to enlarge the arena of power, and at the
same time to complicate the modes of decision-making. The domestic
political process initiated by the New Deal, which continues in the
same form in the domestic program of the Johnson administration,
was in effect a broadening of the "brokerage" system—the system of
political "deals" between constituencies. But there is also a new
dimension in the political process which has given the technocrats a
new role. Matters of foreign policy are not a reflex of internal political
forces, but a judgment about the national interest, involving strategy
decisions based on the calculations of an opponent's strength and
intentions. Once the fundamental policy decision was made to oppose
the Communist power, many technical decisions, based on military
technology and strategic assessments, took on the highest importance
in the shaping of subsequent policy. And even the reworking of the
economic map of the United States followed as well, with Texas and
California gaining great importance because of the importance of the
electronics and aerospace industries. In these instances, technology
and strategy laid down the requirements, and only then could business and local political groups seek to modify, or take advantage of,
these decisions so as to protect their own economic interests.

In all this, the technologists are in a double position. To the extent
that they have interests in research, and positions in the universities,
they become a new constituency—just as the military is a distinct new
constituency, since we have never had a permanent military establishment in this country before—seeking money and support for
science, for research and development. Thus the technical intelligent-
sia becomes a claimant, like other groups, for public support (though
its influence is felt in the bureaucratic and administrative labyrinth,
rather than in the electoral system and through mass pressure). At
the same time, the technologists provide an indispensable administrative mechanism for the political office-holder with his public following. As the technical and professional sectors of society expand, the
interests of this stratum, of this constituency, exert a greater pressure
—in the demands not only for objectives of immediate interest but in
the wider social ethos which tends to be associated with the more
highly educated: the demands for more amenities, for a more urbane

quality of life in our cities, for a more differentiated and better educational system, and an improvement in the character of our culture.

But while the weights of the class system may shift, the nature of the political system, as the arena where interests become mediated, will not. In the next few decades, the political arena will become more decisive, if anything, for three fundamental reasons: we have become, for the first time, a *national society* (though there has always been the idea of the nation) in which crucial decisions, affecting all parts of the society simultaneously (from foreign affairs to fiscal policy) are made by the government, rather than through the market; in addition, we have become a *communal society*, in which many more groups now seek to establish their social rights—their claims on society—through the political order; and third, with our increasing "future orientation," government will necessarily have to do more and more planning. But since all of these involve policy decisions, it cannot be the technocrat alone, but the political figures who can make them. And necessarily, the two roles are distinct, even though they come into complicated interplay with each other.

Irene Taviss

THE TECHNOLOGICAL SOCIETY
Some Challenges for Social Science

It has become a contemporary commonplace that the changes being wrought by modern technology are presenting significant new challenges to man—to his rationality, his morality, his conceptions of the good. But it is becoming equally apparent that these changes also pose new problems for the disciplines engaged in tracking their course. The "post-industrial society" is simultaneously presenting social science with a new public policy involvement and with the need for new conceptual structures. There is thus an increased sense of the relevance of social science at the same time that some of its theoretical underpinnings are becoming increasingly irrelevant or inadequate. The challenge to social science, then, derives from both internal and external sources. Of course, insofar as social science practitioners seek to gain or retain influence in the policy sphere, the two pressures are convergent.

The key features of the technological society that are generating these challenges are: (1) an ethos of planning and the increased use of knowledge in policy-making; and (2) a shift towards increasing public rather than private consumption of goods and a consequent decline in the importance of the market mechanism. These two phenomena are closely interrelated: as the public sector gains in importance relative to the private sector, the market mechanism becomes increasingly irrelevant and planning becomes increasingly necessary.

"The Technological Society: Some Challenges for Social Science" by Irene Taviss. From Social Research (Autumn 1968): 521–39. Reprinted by permission of Social Research.

And as planning mechanisms and procedures are developed, the role of organized knowledge becomes increasingly more salient. Or, looked at from the obverse side: as knowledge is increasingly brought to bear upon policy matters and planning is increasingly implemented, the public sector will grow at the expense of the private sector, thus producing a diminution in the importance of the market mechanism.

Although these changes have been occurring gradually, the thrust provided by modern technology has produced a kind of quantum leap in their development. The growth of modern science and technology is responsible for this post-industrial society in several senses. On the one hand, the affluence resulting from the technology-based growth in productivity has provided the means for meaningful intervention in social and economic processes; and the growth in scientific knowledge has provided at least some of the know-how. On the other hand, the massive resources needed to develop and capitalize upon various large-scale technologies has increasingly led to direct government involvement in the direction and financing of research and development; and the magnitude of the effects of some of these technologies (e.g., pollution, radiation, etc.) has led to the increased involvement of government as regulatory and control agent.

That a shift towards the predominance of the public sector is occurring can be seen in the fact that about one-fourth of GNP and between one-half and two-fifths of all employment is accounted for by the activities of the not-for-profit sector; and nine out of every ten new jobs added to the economy between 1950 and 1960 were generated in this sector.[1] Moreover,

> "[O]ur society has become so rich that the marginal utility of a further increment of productivity, used in the way it is now being used, is small. We can afford a price in efficiency to achieve other goals, if that price must be paid. . . . [There has also been a change] in the nature of what we consume, and especially, the nature of how we perceive what we consume. Goods that are not produced and sold in conventional markets—education and health, for example—are becoming more important in our consumption budget, another reflection of our increasing wealth. Further, we are recognizing increasingly the 'public good' or external interdependency elements in much of our consumption, so that simple acceptance of the view that the market gives the consumers what they want is no longer fully persuasive even in its own terms. We

1. Daniel Bell, "Notes on the Post-Industrial Society (II)," *The Public Interest,* (Spring, 1967), p. 113.

can see this in housing and neighborhood and city planning, or the purchase of automobiles, the building of freeways, and the generation of smog." [2]

That increased planning and the application of knowledge are "in the air" can be attested to by the establishment of such governmental agencies as HEW, HUD, and the Council of Economic Advisers, by the numerous bills currently before the Congress to establish some form of Technology Assessment Board, and by the increasing use by all levels of government of information systems, PPBS, and other scientific decision-making tools. Moreover, piece-meal and merely ameliorative measures to cope with social problems are becoming increasingly suspect, as witness the following *New York Times* editorial comment on the President's 1968 message on the cities:

> ". . . [F]or all the good things in it, the message is an unambitious *status quo* statement. . . . What is needed is what the mathematicians call a quantum leap: A national migration policy to direct the flow of people which now eddies haphazardly from rural backwater to city slum; a national land policy to plan the development of future suburbs and new towns; a national housing policy with much tougher controls over land speculators and featherbedding construction unions." [3]

It must be noted here that the trend towards planning and a public economy is precisely that: a trend. American society is certainly still a long way from being a "planned society." For one thing, Western civilization generally has "nurtured two of its contrary inner tendencies with astonishing care and insistence: One was a deep commitment to detailed molecular disorder, which it cherished as the stepchild of liberty; the other was an almost superstitious belief in the idea of automatism (as exemplified by Adam Smith's 'hidden hand,' or by the extraordinary notion of laissez-faire equilibrium), which it viewed as capable of regulating the disorder into a livable environment. . . . Planning . . . —as informed decision and calculated action—refutes and rejects both these parents. That is why we came to it late and with reluctance; that is why we are still half-hearted about it." [4] Moreover, even if planning was in universal good favor,

2. Carl Kaysen, "The Business Corporation as a Creator of Values," in Sidney Hook (ed.), *Human Values and Economic Policy* (New York: New York University Press, 1967), p. 217.

3. Editorial, *The New York Times,* Feb. 23, 1968.

4. Hasan Ozbekhan, "The Triumph of Technology: 'Can' Implies 'Ought,'" System Development Corporation Professional Paper #SP-2830, June 6, 1967, p. 4.

the road from intent to implementation would not necessarily be a smooth one.

Nevertheless, we are already witnessing a new kind of institutional interdependence that is, at least in part, attributable to these trends. As conventional markets are shrinking, business is increasingly entering the public sphere—building new cities, running Job Corps programs, etc. As scientific knowledge becomes increasingly relevant to policy-making, the universities are increasingly called upon to offer public service through research contracts, the establishment of special research centers, the cooptation of faculty members as consultants and advisers. In addition, a whole host of quasi-public interstitial groups are being spawned—from the aerospace corporations (which, though technically private, have a guaranteed governmental market) to the Rand Corporation and the government-financed university research centers.

How then do these trends impinge upon the enterprise of social science? First of all, on the most general level, both the increasing reliance on social science expertise and the increasing blurring of institutional boundaries point to the need for more research and thinking that is of an interdisciplinary character. As social scientists are called upon to make policy recommendations, they are increasingly dealing with problem-oriented rather than discipline-oriented matters, and the problems under consideration are generally susceptible of attack only through the combined tools and foci of various disciplines. Also, the earlier relatively neat divisions between fields according to the institution being studied become more difficult to maintain in the face of a blurring of institutional lines.

A second general implication for social science is the need to devise sharper measurement instruments and more sophisticated methods of operationalizing variables. Here too the pressures are both internal and external to the social sciences: social scientists cannot be of assistance in the planning process if they cannot provide the tools with which to assess what Bertram Gross has called "the social state of the union"; and social science knowledge of cause and effect cannot be advanced unless ways are found to measure the impact of various programs in order to determine how and why certain of these succeed or fail and to investigate "the unanticipated consequences of social action."

Some degree of responsiveness to these needs is already apparent in the growth of interdisciplinary research teams and in the appearance of the Social Indicators movement. But beyond these two general desiderata, there lie some more fundamental challenges to the conceptual apparatus of economics, political science, and sociology.

New Orientations in Economics

Traditional economics, even as modified by Keynes, is based on the assumption of a market economy. The model is one of individual producers (however large) and individual consumers who act in accordance with their economic interests, as modified by some governmental intervention to keep the system as a whole in good working order. The growth in the relative proportion of the public goods sector thus poses some new questions for economic theory.

> "Individuals have their own scale[s] of values, which allow them to assess relative satisfactions against costs, and to make their purchases accordingly. But public life lacks such ready measures. We cannot ask for and individually buy in the market place our share of unpolluted air. Regulating the availability of higher education by the market alone would deny many families the possibility of such learning, and also deny the society some of the social benefits which a more educated, and therefore more productive, citizenry might create. But we have no effective social calculus which gives us a true sense of the entire costs and benefits of our public initiatives." [5]

Short of developing such a "social calculus," economic theory must modify its assumptions so as to take account of and analyze the diverse impacts of an enlarged public goods sector. A "new economics" must re-examine the nature of the allocation of resources as the government increasingly plays a guiding rather than just an influencing role, as business corporations increasingly devote their energies to public sphere activities, as a higher percentage of the gross national product is given over to the consumption of public goods, and as constraints based on scarcity are lifted.

If the government's role in the economy is changing, so too is the role of the corporation. As at least one observer has noted: ". . . the typical large corporation is already seeking a structure of goals too complex to be described simply as profit maximization and . . . the competive constraints of the markets in which it operates are not so narrow as to preclude a variation in the mix." [6] This statement by

5. Bell, *op. cit.*, p. 103.
6. Kaysen, *op. cit.*, pp. 217–18.

Carl Kaysen was made in the context of a plea for corporations to organize themselves so as to be able to assume greater public responsibility. He argues that, for example,

"... instead of the research and medical staff of a pharmaceutical house asking of a possible new drug only, can we sell it? will it pass the FDA standards? they might ask in addition, will it do something for medicine that existing drugs do not do? enough to be worth the effort of development and marketing? The first pair of questions would continue to be relevant; the second would simply place a more severe constraint on what a firm would be willing to introduce in the way of new drugs." [7]

There are some indications that large corporations are already beginning to assume such responsibility—either voluntarily (as with some restrictions on the production of air pollutants) or under coercion (as in the case of the recent automobile safety legislation). If this is indeed a trend, questions arise which affect the theory of the firm: Do older conceptions of the accountability of management to the shareholders become increasingly less relevant? Is the blurring of the public-private distinction thus a larger question than that created by the development of such quasi-public firms as have arisen in the defense sector?

In one sense, however, the modern business corporation is already an actor of considerable public or political significance:

"The corporate giant not only exercises an influence on the character of the business cycle and on the tastes and habits of the people, but it also exercises considerable authority, along with the Congress and the Pentagon, in deciding which communities will decay and which communities will prosper. It is not an exaggeration to say, therefore, that the large corporation performs a governmental function by sharing with governmental institutions in 'authoritative[ly] allocat-[ing] values for society.' . . . The fact that its decisions have been challenged by government, although infrequently and not always successfully, attests to its political nature." [8]

The regulatory problems created by the size, concentration, and power of major business corporations will become more acute as government economic planning increases in scope. Such planning also has further implications for economic theory. Economists have already

7. *Ibid.*, p. 218.
8. Peter Bachrach, "Corporate Authority and Democratic Theory," in David Spitz (ed.), *Political Theory & Social Change* [sic] (New York: Atherton Press, 1967), p. 257.

become important figures in the policy-making process largely through the mechanism of the Council of Economic Advisers. As planning proceeds further, however, they will increasingly be called upon for analysis, advice, and prediction; for while a certain degree of disorder in the economy was acceptable in the past, today "an irregular and thus unpredictable economic state of affairs has become socially intolerable." [9] If economics is to become a predictive science, amendments of classical theory will have to be made. Indeed, some observers suggest that even such basic tenets of economic theory as the Law of Supply and Demand are no longer adequate. Thus Adolph Lowe argues that the behavior patterns underlying this law—profit maximization and price expectations with less than unit elasticity and quantity expectations with positive expectations—no longer apply. Profit

"maximization has itself lost its classical determinacy, because the time span over which profits are to be maximized can no longer be defined once and for all. In the modern technical and organizational environment, indivisibility of resources, periods of investment and production, the size of financial commitments, etc. vary from branch to branch, possibly from firm to firm and even in one and the same firm from occasion to occasion. Consequently, opposite actions such as an increase or decrease of output, raising or lowering of prices can each be justified as the most promising step for profit maximization." [10]

Moreover,

"[t]he consummation of the Industrial Revolution and the democratization of the Western social systems have liberated the masses from the bondage of extreme scarcity; self-organization of producers, and interventions of governmental policy culminating in the public controls of the welfare state have mitigated the fierceness of competition; and the earlier system of cultural values extolling acquisitiveness is giving way to what by the criterion of the classical laws of the market must be judged as capricious behavior. At the same time large-scale technology and the long-term financial commitments it demands, coupled with the spread of monopoly in the markets of goods and productive services, are progressively immobilizing the flow of resources, thus extending the time span over which dispositions must be made, and

9. Adolph Lowe, "Toward a Science of Political Economics," Position Paper Prepared for The Adolph Lowe Symposium, Mar. 29–30, 1968, New School For Social Research, New York, p. 12.
10. *Ibid.*, p. 20.

reducing the subjective certainty and objective accuracy of business expectations. On the other hand, persistent international tensions and political unrest in many underdeveloped regions, coupled with growing resistance to foreign capital imports in mature economies, preclude the exploitation of vast potential investment opportunities, thus blocking one of the most effective escapement mechanisms of an earlier era." [11]

While the market of today does not operate according to the dictates of classical economics and the market mechanism is losing its earlier dominance, economists will also have to consider the obverse side of the coin: the need to develop market-like mechanisms as the role of government in the economy is enlarged. As a recent editorial in *The Economist* has noted:

> "Up to now most decisions that the frontiers of any particular technology are advanced quite enough have indeed been taken by public opinion. People did not buy super-fast cars; they campaigned against farm chemicals; they don't seem to want to get their food in pills . . . The commercial market reacts to these pressures as free markets are tuned to react. But with governments taking an increasing part in the direction of research and the actual financing of industrial development, the trigger-sharp reactions of a managing director hit in his sales chart are just not there inside ministries. Government machines are geared to take cognisance of the growing points of science; they have little or no machinery for identifying the cut-off point. . . . Unless it is recognised as such, there is a danger that wherever governments take an active part in promoting technology they will be pressing on regardless towards higher and higher peaks of performance long after the social or technical cut-off point has been passed." [12]

New Orientations in Political Science

Questions of corporate responsibility, government regulation, and the development of new market mechanisms in the public goods sector are equally challenging to the political scientist. For if classical economic theory is no longer completely adequate, classical theories of democracy and pluralism are likewise insufficient in the post-industrial society. The blurring of the public-private distinction and of institutional boundaries, the increased use of scientific knowledge and ex-

11. *Ibid.*, p. 23.
12. "The Cut-off," *The Economist*, 226 (Jan. 6, 1968), p. 9.

pertise in public decision-making, and the increased orientation to planning together constitute a change in the nature of our political system which has not yet found adequate expression in political theory. In the policy sphere, as Peter Bachrach has pointed out:

> "[A]t this late date we still seem to be burdened with the Roosevelt-Wilson dilemma: If a concentration of corporate power is not dissipated at the outset it will eventually take over the government agency set up to regulate it. But to attempt to break up the corporate structure into competitive units is to defy an irreversible technological trend. . . . I suspect that among the reasons for our plight is the fact that we lack not only a theory of legitimacy of the giant corporation, but also a viable theory of private power. In my view, the core of the difficulty is an inadequate theory of democracy. Its inadequacy is revealed by the inability of scholars to utilize it in a meaningful way in their analyses of the corporate problem." [13]

American political science has traditionally defined democracy largely in terms of pluralism. The model of the polity is that of competing groups which struggle to maintain or secure power, with the government acting as a kind of broker among them. But in an era of large-scale technology and giant organizations coordination rather than competition becomes increasingly necessary and such a model of the polity is no longer adequate.

> "Whereas the thrust of technology is toward integration, the thrust of American constitutionalism is toward disorganization, and hence ultimately toward stalemate. On the face of it, nothing would seem more likely than that these two seemingly opposed forces should meet in mortal combat. And indeed, we have had collisions between the technological order and the political order in the days of the serious antitrust crusades. But we are beginning to understand why these have always turned out to be sham battles. Although we are only vaguely aware of it, the centripetal forces inherent in technology and the centrifugal forces of our political order are steadily fusing on a new, as yet unnamed level. Until recently, this has been difficult to see. After all, it has been quite within our political tradition to keep these two opposite tendencies in different tracts of life, one labeled public and the other private." [14]

> "When public policy is made at all, it emerges from the quite concerned participation of competing oligarchies. To this fact, tra-

13. Bachrach, *op. cit.*, p. 259.
14. Henry S. Kariel, *The Decline of American Pluralism* (Stanford, Calif.: Stanford University Press, 1967), p. 25.

ditional pluralist theory does not pretend to do justice, for all of its empirical sources and most of its sentiments antedate the modern industrial, economic, and organizational revolutions." [15]

"The current approach [of political science], which soothingly defines our existing political structure as pervasively pluralistic, hypostatizes pluralism. It uses this definition as its point of departure and uncritically treats public and 'private' politics as functional (or dysfunctional) manifestations of a naturally laudable pluralistic social order." [16]

The ever-increasing number of large power blocs intermediate between the individual citizen and the government and the importance of such organizations in policy-making also raise questions concerning the nature of democratic representation. An adequate theory of democracy would have to address itself to problems of organizational democracy—even if these organizations are "private" ones. This is an old problem, raised for example by the growth of powerful and internally undemocratic labor unions. A prevalent argument here has been that however undemocratic the majority of the unions are, their very existence and strength are a boon to democracy since they help to maintain a healthy pluralism. If, however, the notion of pluralism itself becomes suspect in the post-industrial society, then the issue must be raised again in a new light.

Moreover, "the expansion of governmental intervention in the economic and social life of the nation increases the stakes of participation: the government does more, and, therefore, more is to be gained by having a voice over what it does." [17] This phenomenon is reflected in the cries for "participatory democracy" and in the formation of new organizations at all levels of government to implement this desire. To participate effectively in decision-making processes, such organizations are likely to become increasingly centralized and undemocratic—in much the same manner as the unions developed a structure parallel to that of the business corporation in order to act effectively.

The problem of participation in the decision-making process is further compounded by the increasing reliance on scientific and technical knowledge. A political theory adequate to the modern technolog-

15. *Ibid.*, p. 182.
16. *Ibid.*, p. 299.
17. Sidney Verba, "Democratic Participation," in Bertram M. Gross (ed.), "Social Goals and Indicators for American Society: Vol. II," *Annals of the American Academy of Political and Social Science*, 373 (Sept., 1967), p. 55.

ical society will have to confront anew the idea that "knowledge brings power." If the information systems technology currently being adopted by many organizations—public and private and at all levels of government—becomes fully operational and useful in decision-making, then the success of organizations and administrations might well depend on their ability to secure and utilize the best available knowledge.

A development of this kind would have implications for such questions as those concerned with democratic participation (e.g., how will the citizen be able to exert any influence on decision-making? what new rights will have to be guaranteed so as to assure adequate access to relevant information?); the nature of the decision-making structure and process (e.g., will the ground rules for effective decision-making shift? will organizational and political structure be radically altered towards higher degrees of centralization, with implications for federalism and the separation of powers?); and the structure of power in society (e.g., will a scientific or knowledge elite become the primary "power broker"? will access to information and knowledge skills replace wealth as a primary basis of power?). More generally: How will decision-making rationality mesh with processes of political bargaining? In what circumstances will knowledge lead to greater consensus, by eliminating those differing assessments of policies that are based on ignorance, or to greater conflict, by providing reasonable certainty as to the consequences of a given policy and thus bringing questions of differing values and interests into sharper focus? To what extent is the basis of power and authority shifting as science and knowledge gain in social importance and to what extent does science function only as a new legitimizing myth?

The orientation of planning calls into question some traditional assumptions of the American political system. For in many spheres planning brings with it a need for coordination that raises questions about whether our system of federalism and separation of powers as currently constituted is adequate to the demands of modern government. The future-orientation implicit in planning leads to an interest in building new governmental machinery that can act in an anticipatory and not only a reactive fashion—especially in our legal and regulatory institutions.[18] These developments mean that political scientists will be called upon to construct alternative models of organizational structure in order to assess their probable consequences. And

18. *Cf.* for example Harold P. Green, "The New Technological Era: A View From The Law," The George Washington University Program of Policy Studies in Science and Technology, *Monograph No. 1,* Jan. 1968.

political science theory will have to abandon those of its models that are based on an older political system.

New Orientations in Sociology

Just as the questions raised for economics are simultaneously questions of relevance to political science, so the issues of power, authority, and legitimation raised above are equally questions for the sociologist as for the political scientist. But the reliance of the post-industrial society on knowledge and planning also raises some questions that are more peculiarly sociological in nature.

One of the consequences of the orientation of planning is that it brings to the fore questions of values and goals. This occurs in two ways: (1) Value inconsistencies become sharper since one is often forced to choose between competing values as they apply to specific actions and decisions. Thus, for example, the traditional American value problem of equality versus achievement becomes a source of tension in educational planning: do we give all students basically the same education so as to be non-discriminatory or do we gear education to individual achievement and thus make discriminations in what and how we teach students of differing abilities? While this has long been a problem for American education, the development of more deliberate planning brings it into the foreground. (2) Planning brings in its wake the need for a more deliberate spelling out of our values. It raises such questions as for example how much do or should we value leisure as opposed to productivity—or in economic terms, how much potential GNP growth should we forego for the sake of increased leisure. The use of scientific knowledge in the form of new decision-making techniques pushes in the same direction.

> "Using the Defense Department as a model . . . we can glimpse the broadest implications of the new managerial revolution for government and industry. . . . At every level there will be increased pressure to explicate assumptions and goals more clearly and to subject them to quantitative analysis." [19]

But in a more fundamental sense, meaningful planning requires that we ask more basic questions about the nature of values, i.e., that we go beyond such statements as "we value health" or "we value education" and ask, health for what? education for what? etc.

19. Harold L. Wilensky, *Organizational Intelligence: Knowledge and Policy in Government and Industry* (New York: Basic Books, Inc., 1967), p. 184.

"When public health is confronted with the reality that the causes of disease and disability can no longer be successfully isolated and dealt with quite directly, when the health values concerned may no longer be the dominant value consideration, at that point in time public health must either cross over into the new, uncharted territory of the molar, organismic administration of human affairs, or cease to be useful. Actually, although we may cling to the old, we are already more deeply committed to this new course than we may realize. For example, public health can hardly be expected— and has not seriously tried—to eliminate the manufacturing of cigarettes as a means of reducing the incidence of lung cancer. But if the present efforts of public health to modify smoking habits or to isolate the causative agent more directly fail, as they well may, the eventual question will have to be asked: Are we willing and able to make the cultural, socioeconomic, and other adjustments that would be entailed in the necessary control measures? We are inescapably confronted with the determining role of human values. All societies value health, it seems, but for planning programs in a complex society it is necessary to know more than just this. It is necessary to know why, and in relation to what health is valued." [20]

If we are to deal rationally and through the political decision-making process with the multitude of complex questions being raised by organ transplants, longevity, genetics, etc., then we

"must be able to assess the particular liabilities at issue and the probable 'costs' (both immediate, secondary, and beyond) of each proposed course of action in terms of some master conceptualization of the nature of human goals and the various alternative ways of attaining them. . . . [And although] the problem of developing such a plan is, of course, multidisciplinary . . . the most fundamental part of it, the discovery of the underlying and guiding structure, is a challenge to sociology." [21]

In the absence of any such master plan our approach has generally been as follows:

"From inbred notions of the good we have derived a selected number of socioeconomic desirables and translated them into a set of socioeconomic problems. The criterion for translation was the feasible, and the calculus of the feasible was mostly economic in character. . . . What we have failed to do in all this is to ascribe operational meaning to the so-called desirables that motivate us, to

20. Edward S. Rogers, "Public Health Asks of Sociology . . . ," *Science*, 159 (Feb. 2, 1968), p. 507.
21. *Ibid.*, p. 508.

question their intrinsic worth, to assess the long-range consequences of our aspirations and actions, to wonder whether the outcome we seem to be expecting does in fact correspond to that quality of life we say we are striving for—and whether our current actions will lead us there." [22]

"Somehow the ability to link the value of a present act to the value of its chosen consequences must be created and made operational. Only such a link will permit us to determine those ends we should be betting on." [23]

In the face of planning and scientific decision-making, then, questions of the nature of values and of the relationship between knowledge and values are raised in a new context; and the policy-maker looks to the sociologist to shed some light on these questions. What has been the approach of sociological theory to such matters?

At the level of social structure, values are seen as either the shared definitions of the desirable that hold societies together (in the functionalist model) or as the emanations of the interests of the ruling groups imposed on the society as a whole (in the conflict model). At the level of behavior,

"much of the discussion has been both inconclusive and confused. At one pole, values are simply dismissed as either epiphenomenal or else as unknowable by scientifically acceptable operations. . . . At the other pole, behavior would be interpreted as a sheer emanation or expression of values (although this position seems empty of tenants among present-day social scientists). Intermediate positions either take conditions as independent and primary and values as intervening or of minor causal importance, or reverse this formulation." [24]

Some general agreement, however, can be found for the idea that values serve to shape goals, which in turn influence behavior. But thorough explication of the mechanisms which link the three has generally not been attempted. Nor has much attention been paid to the dynamics of value formation, beyond the general idea that values are somehow related to life experiences and living conditions, or to the problem of conflicts or inconsistencies among the different values held by any given society or group, beyond the notion that such inconsistencies are usually not problematic because the conflicting values

22. Ozbekhan, *op. cit.*, p. 9.
23. *Ibid.*, p. 15.
24. Robin M. Williams, Jr., "Individual and Group Values," in Bertram M. Gross (ed.), "Social Goals and Indicators for American Society: Volume I," *Annals of the American Academy of Political and Social Science*, 371 (May, 1967), pp. 25-26.

are applied to different spheres of behavior. In short, questions of the *nature* of values have, by and large, been ignored by contemporary sociology. Whether this has been the case because of the complexities of the subject or because of a sense of irrelevance is open for speculation. But clearly, though the first condition still holds, the second no longer does (if indeed it ever did). For if planning is to mean action taken in the light of values, the nature of the relationship of values to one another, and the nature of the values-goals-action connection become of major importance. And there is need for indicators to measure values and their spread among different elements of the population; for methods for translating values into goals; and for analysis of the consequences for goal x of implementing goal y.

The nature of value formation also becomes a matter of more than academic interest. It is relevant to such questions as: To what extent can or will the government as policy-maker be a generator of values for the society? Conversely, to what extent will the values of an earlier era effectively block the implementation of new policies, and how may or should this be taken into account in the planning process itself? Similarly, might not the old theoretical dispute between the functionalist and conflict theories over the nature of values become more relevant to contemporary life as government agencies increasingly engage in over-all social planning?

The question of the relationship between knowledge and values has been dealt with extensively by Karl Mannheim and other sociologists of knowledge. The general assumption underlying these works is that knowledge is determined, or at least strongly influenced by, the values of the knowledge producers. Few modern social scientists would challenge this basic assumption. But in the post-industrial or "knowledgeable" society[25] this question is raised in a new light. For as Robin Williams has pointed out:

> "A society in which the store of knowledge concerning the consequences of action is large and is rapidly increasing is a society in which received norms and their 'justifying' values will be increasingly subjected to questioning and reformulation." [26]

Thus the obverse of the Mannheimian conception of the knowledge-values relationship might be indicated. Though there is much evidence to show that new knowledge is often either disregarded or reinterpreted to fit existing value patterns, the increasing cognitive and scientific

25. Robert Lane, "The Decline of Politics and Ideology in a Knowledgeable Society," *American Sociological Review*, 31 (Oct., 1966), pp. 649–662.
26. Williams, *op. cit.,* p. 30.

orientation of our culture may be making this increasingly less true. Compounding this is the fact that the increased contact between groups holding differing values—through mobility, the mass media, etc.— may be leading to a more general value consciousness. And heightened consciousness of values may bring with it a degree of value relativism that can produce problems of value grounding or legitimation.[27] A re-opening of the discussion of the nature of values is, then, clearly called for—both because new problems and new questions for sociological theory are being raised and because of the current or potential role of the sociologist as adviser to policy-makers.

Conclusion

There is no doubt that the above discussion has raised many more questions than it attempts to answer. But it has also and deliberately not raised a series of questions of equal importance. These questions pertain to the role of the social scientist as adviser and to the potential promise or danger of the post-industrial society that appears to be emerging. Fortunately, discussion of these issues seems to be under way.

27. For further exploration of this theme see: Irene Taviss, "Alienation: An Exploration Into Its Changing Forms," unpublished Ph.D. dissertation, Harvard University, 1966, ch. 8.

2 / THE IMPACT OF TECHNOLOGY
ON AMERICAN VALUES

In Part 1 we examined the basic properties of the technological society and raised the basic questions about the effects of this society on our values. In this part we proceed to examine how technology affects our values and the dangers in these effects.

The impact of technology on values in our society has been a profound one, but this impact has not been a simple one nor, in most cases, a direct one, as people often assume in their discussions of technology and values. As both Karl Mannheim and Robert Nisbet argue in this part, technology has produced great changes in our values primarily because it has produced basic changes in our everyday lives.

In its early stages *technology, or the rational ordering of means to achieve definite ends,* was largely dominated by the social institutions within which it developed. Technology, especially scientific technology, was first developed in the realm of warfare and served the ends of making warfare more "effective"; that is, more total and deadly. But as the industrial revolution gained momentum, technology became a basic driving force. Not only did the whole idea of technology become basic to the modes of production of industry, but science and engineering, certainly by the nineteenth century, had become a basic source of new ideas for things to be produced. The crucial development in the impact of technology on values came through this growing separation and independence of technology from its original sources. As Nisbet argues, technology became an autonomous set of social ideas and practices. Individuals and organizations dedicated themselves to the advancement of technology for its own sake, and segments of society other than the military and industry began to adopt technology for their own purposes. In this way, technology came to permeate most of the basic institutions of society, such as government, the universities, and religion.

As technology becomes ever more an integral part of social processes of society and comes to affect our everyday lives, it impinges on values in our lives. Technology creates new possibilities of action and in so doing creates many possible conflicts with older patterns of behavior, and thereby, with associated values.

As Max Weber long ago realized, technology is merely a special part of the generalized process of *rationalization* that has been taking place in the Western world over the last several centuries. As rationalization and technology progress throughout our society, they not only come into conflict with other values but undermine the effectiveness of those values in many ways. Most importantly, as Nisbet argues, the values and ideas of technology undermine other values by leading the members of society to take an increasingly abstract and generalized view of evaluations.

Many social thinkers and sociologists, such as Hanna Arendt and Karl Mannheim, have argued that technology has so affected basic forms of thought and action in our society that they have transformed much of our society. Mannheim is also one of those who believes technology has so affected our values that it has produced a crisis in valuation; that is, it has made evaluation of alternatives in any situation extremely problematic, if not impossible. In his essay, "The Crisis in Valuation," he presents industrialization and the development of technology as merely two of the seven basic causes of this crisis. Yet it is important to note that most of his other "fundamental factors" are themselves the products of the development of technology in our society. For example, it is technology that has been largely responsible for the growth of the size of our society and the growth in the different kinds of contacts members of our society have. Technology has produced these changes primarily by making the medical revolution possible, which leads to the rapid increase in population, and by producing the electronics revolution that makes it possible for us to be in direct contact with much of the world through international television and radio.

Having examined the general effects of technology on our values and the most general threats of technology involved in these effects, we shall proceed in each of the succeeding parts to consider the more specific threats of technology to our values and our form of government.

Robert Nisbet

THE IMPACT OF TECHNOLOGY
ON ETHICAL DECISION-MAKING

Technology, like any other force, has moral consequences only when it becomes a part of the effective normative environment. Considered solely in its mechanical aspects, technology is no more capable than the raw, physical environment of directly affecting cultural and moral consciousness. It may have a broadening or limiting effect on economic and social possibilities—and therewith on ethical alternatives—but it will not become a significant ethical force until it is involved in a pattern of social meanings central to society.

This is, I think, the basic and lasting point that Max Weber made in his critique of Marx's account of the origins of capitalism in the West. Despite certain inadequacies in Weber's application of the point to the causal relation between puritanism and capitalism, the essence of his value theory, applied to historical change, can scarcely be challenged. Only when technology becomes institutionalized, only when technology becomes itself a social system, subject to processes common to all social systems, can we discover its impact on ethical decisions.

"The Impact of Technology on Ethical Decision-Making" by Robert Nisbet. From Robert Lee and Martin E. Marty, eds., Religion and Social Conflict *(New York: Oxford University Press, Inc., 1964), pp. 183–202. Copyright © 1964 by Oxford University Press, Inc. Reprinted by permission of the publisher.*

The Place of Technology in Contemporary Life

There has never been a time since man emerged from the higher primates when he has not been in possession of at least a minimal degree of technology, and so were created the first earthen pot, the spear, and the mortar. Behind the appearance of each of these lay some extraordinary mind, restless and dissatisfied, working in terms of its own and other observations, striving to bring environment within control, to facilitate the business of living. In our own overwhelmingly technological age there is often a danger that we will underestimate the role of technology in other ages. We must not, for it has always been present in one degree or another in human history.

So much is true, yet it must be emphasized that in no other age of history has technology held the central and determining role that it does in our own. Never have so many persons been involved so directly in technological pursuits. At no time in the human past has the technologist-scientist held the crucial role that he does today. Marvel though we may at the ingenious accomplishments of Hellenistic Greece, Imperial Rome, the late Middle Ages, and the Renaissance, they are small indeed by comparison with the works of the modern age.

What philosophy, theology, and art have been in other periods—the major contexts of human creativity—technology is today. Each age produces its own type of hero: soldier, diplomat, theologian, scholar, statesman, or businessman. Today, who would deny that the technologist occupies the hero's niche? Nobel laureates, National Academy members, scientist-administrators, all possess a prestige that makes front page news and carries them to the highest councils of government and society. The time has passed when technology needs to justify itself by its contributions to other spheres of society. Today the ends of technology are sufficient and autonomous.

More important is the fact that in the modern West, for the first time in history, technology has become institutionalized. An institution is a way of behavior, common to a large number of persons in a society. Handed down from generation to generation, it is a generally recognized solution to a recognized problem. In every relevant respect, technology today is as fully and distinguishably an institution as law, religion, or kinship. It is neither more nor less "material" than other institutions. There is no more reason for limiting technology, as a concept, to the machines and tools it employs than there is for limiting the family to housing, law to court rooms, or religion to church buildings.

What is central to technology is the application of rational principles to the control or re-ordering of space, matter, and human beings. We are prone to think of technology in its physical manifestations—skyscrapers, lawn mowers, nuclear bombs—but technology represents social things as well—organizations and processes concerned with human ends. There is as much technology in a school of business administration or education as there is in a school of engineering. The one is as concerned as the other with the rational and calculated achievement of ends which, more and more in our society, are autonomous and self-justifying ends.

This last point may require brief justification. Surely, it will be said, the ends of technology are subordinate to those of economy, religion, politics, and war—all older and more accepted areas of human purpose. This was true, once, but it is no longer true. The conquest of space, the control of physical environment, the mastery of organization, are objectives today fully as distinct as any to be found in the classic areas of statecraft, war, and business.

Innumerable foundations, institutes, vast research and development laboratories, not to mention huge budgets for technological development, all attest to the autonomy as well as prestige of technology. Admittedly, military defense is the context of a great deal of present-day technology, but I would argue that technological imperatives have attained a degree of primacy not likely to be offset by any changes in the international scene.

Modern technology has its own characteristic structures, its built-in drives, its moral codes, its dedicated servants (as hierarchically ordered and motivated as any to be found in church or state), even its own mystique. Because technology serves an autonomous set of values in our society, and because it is itself a clear pattern of functions and authorities, it inevitably comes into moral conflict with other institutions in society. The tension that Thorstein Veblen was able to discern a half-century ago between the engineer and the price system has become a not uncommon tension between technology and other areas of society—political, esthetic, religious, as well as economic.

Until perhaps a century ago, technology was only an instrumental value. Its significance came from the institution it served. Throughout much of the modern era, especially in the nineteenth century, this significance was economic. Hence the still almost synonymous use of the words "industrial" and "technological."

But before industry, technology served the needs of war. The word engineer was indeed so closely identified with military activities from the fifteenth century on that it became necessary in the late eighteenth century to prefix it by the word "civil" in order to specify a non-military orientation. But quite apart from its earlier ancillary function in society, technology is today an autonomous pattern of ends, functions, authorities, and allegiances.

From the point of view of the history of social institutions, there is nothing extraordinary in this process of "autonomization." We can see it in the histories of religion, politics, and education. In the early Roman Republic, religion, far from being a separate institution, was simply one function of the family. The chief end of religion under the *patria potestas* was that of welding the family into a unity, not merely in space but in time. But as we know, religion became, at a later period in Rome, a separate and autonomous institution; and in its Christian form, a powerful rival to both family and state.

The same transition may be seen in economic processes. In many cultures, economics is subordinate to some other institution: family, religion, or community. It is ethnocentric to assume, as did the classical economists in the nineteenth century, that economic ends and processes are everywhere sovereign and independent. In the West, since approximately the Enlightenment, economic institutions have been autonomous, though this situation shows signs in our own age of undergoing significant change.

As an institution, technology has today, then, its own function: the rational control of man, space, and matter—and its own governing values. It is no stretch of meaning, I suggest, to hold that technology has sacred overtones in the minds of many. To contravene the values of technology in favor of, say, nationalism or economic profits can seem as impious to a scientist today as contravention of religious ends, in the name of economic gain, seemed to a medieval theologian.

Ethics and Social Conflict

Because technology in our society is an institution and because ethical decisions are closely related to what happens to institutions, it is important at this point to examine briefly the character of institutional change. It is my contention that conflict is the essence of such change. And it is in circumstances of institutional change that ethical values become most luminous.

Too often institutions are conceived as structures endowed with immanent tendencies toward change. They are regarded much as the biologist regards organic life—as something inherent in growth and development, with new phases arising directly and inexorably out of the old. For a long time this organic analogy has plagued Western social thought and confused the study of change in society.

Institutions are complexes of functions, authorities, and values, and apart from their interaction with other institutions—competitive and conflicting interaction—there is no reason to suppose that significant change in any one of them takes place.

In all institutional behavior there is a powerful tendency toward integration and conformity, resulting from the implicit striving of each institution for the total allegiance of its members. What Frank Tannenbaum has written along this line is instructive:

> Each institution in its own inner logic tends to be all-embracing, laying claim to the entire man, and showing an impelling tendency to assume all responsibility in society . . . Institutional friction and instability are, therefore, the normal state of society, and the hope of peace and quietude is an idle dream. Competition, imbalance, and friction are not merely continuous phenomena in society, but in fact, are evidences of vitality and "normality." [1]

Conflict and competition in the institutional scene are inevitably reflected in the minds and moral aspirations of the persons concerned. Institutional conflict is matched by the conflict of human loyalties. Conflict of this type can sometimes be drastic and difficult, as we know from the frequently agonizing experiences of immigrants involved in the transplating of mores and life-patterns from one culture to another. Much of American social history is made up of this transplanting and with it there has been frequent conflict of institutional and moral loyalties. Out of such conflicts, to be sure, have come some of the great intellectual and moral achievements of American civilization, but out of them have also come some of our bitterest social and moral problems.

In the orthodox, rationalist tradition, little attention was paid to change considered as crisis and to the persisting conflicts of values among institutions of the same society. The gospel of homogeneity and adjustment held the field. That a plurality of institutions could exert powerful and possibly irreconcilable conflicts of allegiance upon individuals was not often envisaged by those who saw change as a smooth and orderly process.

1. Frank Tannenbaum, "The Balance of Power in Society," *Political Science Quarterly* (December 1946).

Nevertheless the conflict is there, and it is a fact of the highest significance in history. Sometimes this conflict is passive, awakening only vague sensations of tension. Elements of persistence and conformity in the individual may reduce the effects of conflict on his allegiances. At other times it may be fierce and overt, reflected in widespread mass upheaval and in the central problems of moral philosophies.

Such conflicts, small and large, do not, as the progressive rationalist has thought, resolve themselves inevitably into systems of new coherence and order—either in the individual consciousness or in the overt relationships of major institutions. Where they are matters of crucial allegiance—as with respect to family, church, ethnic group, and state—they may remain for centuries, now relatively passive, now evocative and fiercely antagonistic.[2]

Ethical history is fundamentally a history of the conflict of social loyalties. How else do we account for the history of moral values in ancient Athens except in terms of the struggle between the ancient kinship group and the new city-state? The fifth century B.C. was a time of the breaking up of ancient kinship structures and the gradual emergence of the individual as ethical man, as political man. The reforms of Cleisthenes a century earlier had led to the reduced political position of tribe and clan, but the moral appeal of these groups and their implicit and ancient norms remained binding for the Athenian.

It was in the gradual diminution of kinship norms and the simultaneous rise of the free individual and the popular state that the great moral issues of the age found their setting. Of all ethical problems the greatest was individual responsibility. This is the recurrent theme of the dramas of Aeschylus, Sophocles, and Euripides. How is guilt to be assigned? To the individual, as the new legal polity suggested? Or collectively—to family and clan—as ancient tradition had it? This was the great conflict in the fifth century, and it would be difficult to understand either the moral philosophers or the dramatists apart from it.[3]

In Roman civilization we see the conflict between the family and the military power, between *patria potestas* and *imperium*. In political terms it is a conflict for power over individuals and property. In

2. See my *The Quest for Community* (New York: Oxford University Press, 1953), Chapter 4.

3. The best treatments of this are Gustave Glotz, *La Solidarité de la famille dans le droit criminel en Grèce* (Paris: A Fontemoing, 1904) and Louis Gernet, *Droit et société dans la Grèce ancienne* (Paris: Sirey, 1955).

social terms it is a conflict of statuses—the status of the son under kinship authority and the status of the son as soldier under the *imperium*.

Ethically, the conflict is to be seen in the problem of both where guilt lies—in family or in the individual—and where the sanctions for violation of norms lie—in the family or in the state. The conflict reached its zenith in the final century of the Republic, a period of pandemic disorganization, and was resolved, legally at least, by Augustus' far-reaching decrees on morals which for once and all, put moral sanctions in the hands of the state.

But the diminution of the moral authority of the family was one of the factors leading to the attractiveness of Christianity to Roman masses. By the second century, the struggle between church and state characterized the ethical history of Rome, which was not moderated until Constantine's conversion.[4]

In various ways the conflict of institutions continued in the periods that followed in the West. In the early Middle Ages, at a time when the church sought to Christianize the Teutons, the struggle was between church and clan. It was a conflict between two inner ethical orders—the moral order of the family and the moral order of the church.

Expressed most concretely in such matters as rights over baptism, marriage, and disposition of the dead, the struggle manifested itself in a host of ways, all related to functions and authority within each institution, and to the loyalties which these two institutions were able to attract. In the process of its eventual victory over kinship, the church took on many of the attributes of an enlarged family.[5]

The triumph of the church in matters of individual conduct was short-lived, for, as we know, by the thirteenth century political power began to challenge religious power. Here was perhaps the most fundamental and implicative conflict in the whole history of the West. At first it looked as though the church would win—consider the monumental significance of Canossa. In the long run, however, the centralizing, nationalizing tendencies of the state could not be stayed. Again we see, as we did in Athens, the simultaneous emergence of the individual and the state, each freed, increasingly, from the legal and moral bonds of medieval traditionalism.

4. I have dealt with this at greater length in my "Kinship and Political Power in First Century Rome," pp. 203–24.

5. The best of all treatments of medieval institutions and the conflicts among them is Edward Jenks, *Law and Politics in the Middle Ages* (New York: Henry Holt, 1898).

In the twentieth century such conflicts continue, and are to be seen in court cases involving the competing claims of church or family against state in such matters as flag observances in the schools, released time for worship, military service, and other matters. On a vaster and profounder scale they are to be seen in countries where totalitarianism has taken command; here the old conflict between the state and social groups is converted from something latent or intermittent to something that is at the very heart of freedom and morality. The struggle between family and state, between church and state, between trade union and state was vivid in the early days of National Socialism in Germany. It was only when the Nazi state destroyed or completely fettered these competing groups that its own power could be called totalitarian.

So, too, in the non-Western societies throughout the twentieth century, do we see institutional conflict that is deeply moral and spiritual in result. Sidney Nettleton Fisher has concretely expressed this conflict as it appears in the Near East:

> At the heart of the tension is the clash of family and national loyalties. The family or the clan has been the basic unit of Near Eastern society for millennia: The ecumenical context in which these units have been more or less loosely welded together has been the religious commune to which they gave allegiance and in which they cooperated for larger ends. Yet today the nation state and militant nationalism are thrust between these two, claiming to overarch, if not indeed to supersede them. There emerge tensions and fears, hesitation and irresolution on the part of individuals and groups who suspect, generally unconsciously, their ancient values are threatened, and therefore they draw back from wholehearted allegiance to the nation, at least to the nation's claimant representative. Just when the state or government wishes and needs to prevent a strong front against some opposition or threat, so often a politician's or statesman's family and communal ties will interfere and hopelessly tangle the web of decision.[6]

The conflict between Western and non-Western cultures is, as A. J. Toynbee has written, the single most important fact of the twentieth century. In whatever form it first expresses itself, political, economic, or technological, it becomes inevitably moral and spiritual: it becomes a tension of ethical norms and judgments.

Normative loyalties tend to become directed toward the spheres which have the greatest significance in maintaining life and integra-

6. S. N. Fisher, *Social Forces in the Middle East* (Ithaca: Cornell University Press, 1955), p. 258.

tive social meanings. Although never a crude relationship, there is a close relationship between the spiritual appeal of symbols and the extent to which symbols are rooted in the effective social community. As Susanne Langer has written:

> The mind, like other organs, can draw its sustenance only from the surrounding world; our metaphysical symbols must spring from reality. Such adaptation always requires time, habit, tradition, and an intimate knowledge of a way of life. If now the field of our unconscious symbolic orientation is suddenly plowed up by tremendous changes in the external world and in the social order, we lose our hold, our convictions, and therewith our effectual purposes.[7]

This plainly is what is happening to large parts of the non-Western world at the present time, and the results are frequently to be seen in cultural disorganization and moral confusion. The wresting of economic significance from clans or social classes; the withdrawal of political power from the tribe; the introduction of a new administrative or technological system in a native area; all of this can have deep moral consequences.

Technological Processes and Ethical Decision-Making

Let us return to technology and to some of the specific forms of its impact on society and ethics. In the foregoing pages I have emphasized two major points: 1. Technology will significantly affect human behavior only as it ceases to be something external and becomes internalized in a culture, a recognized part of norms and institutions. 2. Conflict, in one degree or another, is the essence of social change, and ethical conflicts are themselves manifestations of institutional struggle for functional dominance and superiority.

There is an abundant literature in history, anthropology, and sociology documenting the impact of technology on culture and social institutions. As one surveys this literature, there are four distinguishable processes, it seems to me, which represent the common and even predictable effects of technology. Naturally, they do not work alone. Technology never enters a culture, or makes its rise within a culture, apart from political and economic currents which provide contexts. Nevertheless, the technological processes are distinguishable and im-

7. Susanne Langer, *Philosophy in a New Key, A Study in the Symbolism of Reason, Rite, and Art* (New York: New American Library, 1948), p. 237.

portant. They are: abstraction, generalization, individuation, and rationalization.

1. The first of these I choose to call *abstraction*. I mean by this the separation of moral values from the contexts of immediacy and concreteness that they tend to have in traditional, pre-technological society. The norms of science and technology are abstract and impersonal, and their net effect, over a period of time, can be to make other values seem less urgent, less sacred in character, and more like propositions of utility. Moral behavior is concrete and personal; it is tied to sharply defined symbols in the community which draw their own efficacy from essentially non-rational sources. The more abstract and remote, the more impersonal and utilitarian these symbols become, the less urgency they have to individuals.

There is also the key role in traditional society of *social membership*. Norms arise from and are inseparable from the close groups in which individuals have membership. It is never man as man, but man as member of clan, tribe, guild, or class that is important. The ethical values are properties of these close and influential groups.

In the kind of society that technology helps create, however, human identity does not rest exclusively on the small and personal type of association. It tends increasingly to come from qualities which the individual holds in common with large numbers of other persons whom he never sees or knows, persons who fall into abstract categories.

Ostrogorski has described this vividly in his treatment of the impact of technology on modern Europe.

> In proportion as the new conditions of existence enlarged the social horizon in the sphere of life, just as it expanded by means of thought, the process of abstraction extended to all social relations. The rapid growth of large towns destroyed the old neighborly intercourse, or at all events, its intimate character. The extension of markets stripped buyers and sellers of their concrete individuality, and resolved them into the general categories of *tradesmen* and *customers*. Railways, by bringing together for half an hour men who saw each other for the first and perhaps the last time, reduced them to the general notion of *travelers*, all placed on an equal footing by uniform tickets, a piece of pasteboard printed wholesale for all present and future travelers. In great industrial enterprises creative energy and active will associated in the form of *shares*, negotiable securities, transferable to an infinite series of potential entities existing only as *shareholders*. Even the feelings which take their rise in the depths of the soul, such as the love of one's neighbor and pity, were obliged, when projected over a larger area to conform to abstract notions; the familiar picture of the wretched Jim or Tom who had been the

regular recipient of relief, gave place to the idea of the poor man, the poorer classes.[8]

The Hammonds, writing with particular reference to the impact of technology on England in the nineteenth century, could see the machine in the guise of a new rhythm and tempo of life. Gone was the rhythm of the rural countryside, based upon the direct experience of the passing of the seasons, the rising and setting of the sun, the planting and harvesting of the crops. In its place now was the rhythm of the machine, the never-ending turning of the wheels and gears. Behind the rhythm represented by the factory bell and the overseer, the precise division of the day into units of wages-time, and the machine itself, there lay, as the Hammonds emphasized, the great, impersonal system within which human beings congregated not as members of a moral community but as so many abstract units of energy and production, rationally organized for specific, mechanical purposes.[9]

2. Closely related to abstraction is a second process, *generalization.* Again it is illuminating to quote Ostrogorski.

> Confined hitherto to the narrow range of his social circle, it (the moral sentiment) now spread further and further beyond these limits; the tribunal of public opinion sat in judgment wherever cognizance could be taken of the individual's conduct; at the bar of his conscience man became responsible not only to his own society in the restricted sense of the word, but to society in general, to his country, to the nation, even to humanity. Thus a readjustment of forces took place in man's social existence between the particular which constituted nearly all his being and the general which occupied but a small portion of it. Destined as he is by his finite and limited frame to cling to the concrete and the particular as his starting point and strongest support, man nevertheless launched on all sides into the general, with the result that henceforth his social relations were bound to be guided not so much by sentiment, which expresses the perception of the particular, as by general principles, less intense in their nature perhaps, but sufficiently comprehensive to take in the shifting multitudes of which the abstract social groups were henceforth composed, groups continually subject to expansion by reason of their continual motion.[10]

8. M. Ostrogorski, *Democracy and the Organization of Political Parties* (New York: Macmillan, 1902), Vol. 1, pp. 45 ff.

9. J. L. and Barbara Hammond. See esp. *The Town Laborer* (London: Longmans, Green, 1917), *passim.*

10. Ostrogorski, *op. cit.,* pp. 49–50.

In one of the most illuminating chapters of his *Democracy in America,* Tocqueville has shown how the concept of honor, beginning as a fundamental value of one class alone, the nobility, and drawing its sustenance from feudal contexts of authority, becomes steadily more general in modern times. Tocqueville concludes:

> When ranks are comingled and privileges abolished, the men of whom a nation is composed being once more equal and alike, their interests and wants become identical, and all the peculiar notions which each caste styled honor successively disappear. The notion of honor no longer proceeds from any other source than the wants peculiar to the nation at large, and it denotes the individual character of that nation to the world . . . As honor among democratic nations is imperfectly defined, its influence is of course less powerful; for it is difficult to apply with certainty and firmness a law that is not distinctly known.[11]

What Tocqueville writes of honor is not less true of a large number of other values—loyalty, integrity, guilt and innocence, patriotism, piety. In each instance we are dealing with a norm that arose in the first instance within clear and decisive contexts. Generally, they were the contexts of small association. Morality, as we have noted, was indistinguishable from the inner order of clan, village, or class. It was as concrete as it was associative, and because it was concrete it had meaning in the daily lives of individuals.

In the same way that the development of the political community has meant the generalization and abstraction of all the local and particularized authorities which traditional society abounded in, so the spread of technology has meant the generalization and abstraction of the various norms which, in earlier times, had been limited to small communities. The same technology which made possible mass society made possible mass norms—another way of referring to generalization and abstraction.

3. A third process to be noted is *individuation.* Technology is one of the modern forces that have had a frequently fragmenting and dissolving effect upon traditional communities. Because technology is itself a social system, with a place in it for the individual conceived in a new status, it has an individualizing effect upon the older communities. By virtue of the abstract and impersonal character of the technological system, the individual is able to perceive himself more

11. Alexis de Tocqueville, *Democracy in America* (New York: Knopf, 1945), Vol. 2, bk 3, ch. 18.

vividly as a separate being rather than as an organic member of a community. The late G. P. Adams wrote:

> It is not strange that the self discovery and self consciousness of the individual should have steadily mounted higher as the environment of the individuals more and more takes on the form of an impersonal, causal, and mechanical structure. For the mobility and freedom of the individual can be won only as he becomes detached from his world; his world becomes separated from him only when organized and defined in objective and impersonal terms.[12]

Such sociologists as Tönnies, Simmel, Durkheim, and Weber have all emphasized the processes of modern history that have led to a mechanization and atomization of the primary social relationships. No doubt it is easy to exaggerate this, and we cannot forget that technology has synthesized even as it has fragmented, but it remains true that the very impersonality and abstractness of technology formed a background against which the individual could seem more real than the primary and communal ties from which he was being separated.

The rationalist image of society in this age powerfully supported the individualizing tendencies of the new technology. In man alone were now placed virtues and stabilities that had earlier developed within associations. How else, rationalists asked, could the moral imperatives of emancipation be fulfilled except by the premise of man's separateness and his autonomy? The demands of freedom appeared to be in the direction of the release of large numbers of individuals from the statuses and identities that had been created for them by history. A free society would be one in which individuals were morally and socially as well as politically free, free from ancient traditions and corporate groups. Order in society would be the product of a natural equilibrium of economic and political forces, just as order in technology itself is the result of an equilibrium of levers and gears.

4. To these three processes I would add one more that seems to me deeply embedded in the impact of technology on society: *rationalization*.[13] Here I am referring to the widespread tendency throughout modern society to bring under the formal rules of hierarchical

12. G. P. Adams, *Idealism and the Modern Age* (New Haven: Yale University Press, 1919), p. 35.
13. It was, of course, Max Weber whose writings first identified and documented this process in modern European history.

administration areas of thought and behavior which have been traditionally areas of informal and individual decision-making. Rationalization of decision-making is plainly a deep tendency in education and religion as well as in industry and the state.

The very progress of modern administrative techniques has created a problem in the maintenance and nurture of individual thought and action. In the same way that the technological revolution reduced man's significance through the transfer of, first, strength, then skill, and finally thought itself, to the machine, it now appears to have a fourth phase: one in which individual decision is being transferred to the machine—conceived as scientific and channeled organization. By its very triumph of rationality, scientific administration has reduced much of the elbow room, much of the intellectual and moral friction which ethical individuality must have if it is to flourish.

In one of his essays, the distinguished physicist, P. W. Bridgman, now retired, tells us that it becomes steadily more difficult for him to conceive the emergence of great *individual* physicists in our age of science, simply because of the increasing involvement of so much scientific research in the costly and elaborate machinery of administrative organization. Such administration, and all that it implies, can too often take away the informal and challenging atmosphere that creative people need.

Ethical decision-making is, from one point of view, a form of creativity, and it is no exaggeration to suggest that it may suffer in related ways. Quite apart from the time-consuming complexity of much administration, it can contain a kind of tyranny. The tyranny consists of tiny rules governing action and decision; of innumerable channels and levels; of committees and all the other types of rational administration which, however effective they may be from a purely technical point of view, powerfully affect the ethical role of the individual. Ethical decision-making, like leadership, requires a certain degree of autonomy from the rules, an opportunity for occasional error and an understanding that the individual himself, not the organization, bears responsibility.

Decision-making, as Robert Presthus has recently written, becomes vague and impersonal in the big organization, the instrument of an anonymous, fragmented intelligence.

> Each decision is the result of various technical and personal considerations, the sum of the contributions of the sum of everyone involved in the deciding process. This diffusion means that "everyone" (i.e., no one) is responsible. In extreme cases the condition may lead to arbitrary and immoral behavior, particularly when com-

pounded by intense personal identification with the state, the party, the church, or the "organization." In every case, the probabilities that the organization may act unjustly are increased by the weakening of individual responsibility. Only "the system" is responsible.[14]

In a brilliant article, Harold Rosenberg has recently dealt with the Eichmann trial in these terms. Mr. Rosenberg points out that Eichmann's defense was based almost entirely on a proposition that he knew could not help but have appeal to large numbers of persons in our society. Basically, this defense rested on his transference of guilt from himself, as an individual, to a soulless, impersonal organization within which he was but a simple cog. Guilt, as we have known the concept throughout most of history, is individual, and thereby requires a sense of the self. But if the self is obliterated, if the organization takes command, reducing individuals to roles without responsibility, how can there be guilt? The very essence of the Nazi system was the blurring and extinguishing of the sense of the self. And as Eichmann shrewdly realized, this has become a pervading characteristic of the modern technological world.

> Eichmann's defense was designed to appeal to the universal appreciation of the plight of the organization man. Who cannot grasp that one in the middle of a chain of command—a link in the sausage—simply passes down orders he receives from above, without having the power to alter their content or to influence their ultimate effects? Everyone in an organization is in a sense nothing but a traffic officer while the directors at the top reach decisions that reflect a collective mind separate from that of each . . . It is not thinkable to be the dispatcher of human shipments to death factories but by analogy with the clean hands of the office man in charge of shipping fertilizer or veal carcasses, it *is* thinkable.[15]

Conclusion

We conclude where we began. Technology viewed simply as the machine is powerless to affect human culture or ethics. Only as it becomes institutionalized, only as its ends conflict with and override established norms, does technology become a dislocating and moulding force in society. Technology need not weaken individuality in society—not any more than physical landscape need weaken it. But

14. Robert Presthus, *The Organizational Society* (New York: Knopf, 1962), pp. 53–54.
15. Harold Rosenberg, "The Eichmann Trial," *Commentary* (November 1961).

when its institutionalization reaches the point of reducing the normal conflict of institutions through techniques of abstraction, generalization, and rationalization, it may be regarded as posing a threat to individuality and to ethical decision-making. Technology becomes one of the forces in society whereby the individuality and concreteness of ethical norms—such norms as honor, guilt, loyalty—become tenuous and indistinct.

The making of ethical decisions is always related to conflict of one kind or another: there is a conflict of *institutions* in society or a conflict of *ends* in the individual consciousness. It is unlikely that without the large institutional conflict, any significant inner conflict of ends and meanings could occur. Within the very circumstances which helped liberate individuality from the older traditional types of community, the key problem of the present age, I believe, is that of maintaining individuality of ethical decision-making.

Karl Mannheim

THE CRISIS IN VALUATION

I. Conflicting Philosophies of Life

At first only a few people were aware of the approaching chaos and the crisis in our system of valuations. They noticed that the religious and moral unity which integrated mediaeval society was vanishing. Still, the disintegration was not yet quite apparent, because the Philosophy of Enlightenment seemed to offer a new approach to life with a unified purpose, out of which developed the secularized systems of Liberalism and Socialism. No sooner had we made up our mind that the future would resolve itself into a struggle for supremacy between these two points of view than a new system of valuation emerged, that of universal Fascism. The basic attitude of the new outlook is so different from that of the previous systems that their internal differences seem almost to vanish.

Thus, in the very same social environment we now have the most contradictory philosophies of life. First, there is the religion of love and universal brotherhood, mainly inspired by Christian tradition, as a measuring-rod for our activities. Then there is the philosophy of Enlightenment and Liberalism, with its emphasis on freedom and personality, and its appreciation of wealth, security, happiness, tolerance and philanthropy as the means of achieving them. Then we have the challenge of the Socialists, who rate equality, social justice, basic security and a planned social order as the chief desiderata of

"The Crisis in Valuation." From Diagnosis of Our Time: Wartime Essays of a Sociologist *by Karl Mannheim (New York: Humanities Press, Inc.; London: Routledge & Kegan Paul Ltd., 1943), pp. 12–26. Reprinted by permission of the publishers.*

the age. But beyond all this we have, as I said before, the most recent philosophy, with the demoniac image of man emphasizing fertility, race, power, and the tribal and military virtues of conquest, discipline and blind obedience.

We are not only divided against each other in our evaluation of the big issues, such as the principles of the Good Life and those of the best social organization, but we have no settled views, especially in our democratic societies, concerning the right patterns of human behaviour and conduct. One set of educational influences is preparing the new generation to practise and defend their rational self-interest in a competitive world, while another lays the emphasis on unselfishness, social service and subordination to common ends. One set of social influences is guided by the ideal of asceticism and repression, the other by the wish to encourage self-expression.

We have no accepted theory and practice concerning the nature of freedom and discipline. Some think that, owing to the self-regulating powers inherent in group life, discipline would spontaneously emerge if only full freedom were given and the pressure of external authority removed. In contrast to this anarchist theory, others hold that if strict regulation is applied to those spheres of life where it is necessary, the scope for real freedom is not suppressed but rather created. To such thinkers discipline is the pre-condition of freedom. Having no settled views on freedom and discipline, it is not surprising that we have no clear-cut criteria for the treatment of criminals, and do not know whether punishment should be retributive and deterrent or a kind of readjustment and re-education for life in society. We hesitate whether to treat the law-breaker as a sinner or as a patient, and cannot decide whether he or society is at fault.

But the crisis in valuations does not only come to the fore in marginal cases of maladjustment such as crime; we have no agreed educational policy for our normal citizens, since the further we progress the less we know what we are educating for. On the primary levels of education we are undecided whether to aim at creating millions of rationalists who discard custom and tradition and judge each case on its merits, or whether the chief aim of education should be the handing on of that social and national inheritance which is focussed in religion. On the higher levels of education we do not know whether to educate for specialization, which is urgently needed in an industrialized society with a strict division of labour, or whether we should cater for all-round personalities with a philosophical background.

Again, it is not only in the world of education that we are hazy;

we are equally vague concerning the meaning and value of work and leisure. The system of working primarily for profit and monetary reward is in process of disintegration. The masses are craving for a stable standard of living, but over and above that, they want to feel that they are useful and important members of the community, with a right to understand the meaning of their work and of the society in which they live. While this awakening is going on amongst the masses, there is a split in the ranks of the wealthy and educated few. To some their high position and accumulated wealth means primarily the enjoyment of limitless power; to others, an opportunity for applying their knowledge or skill, giving guidance, shouldering responsibility. The first group represent the potential leaders of Fascism, the latter are those who are willing to assist in building up a new social order under competent leadership.

As I have said it is not only work but also leisure that is subjected to entirely different interpretations and valuations. The puritan sense of guilt in connection with leisure and recreation is still at war with the emerging hedonistic cult of vitality and health. The idea of privacy and contemplation, and of their value, is at war with that of mass enjoyment and mass ecstasy. The same division of opinion appears in regard to our sex habits. Some still condemn sex altogether, trying to place it under a taboo, while others see a remedy for most of our psychological maladjustments in the removal of mystery and repression from that sphere of life. Our concepts and ideals of femininity and masculinity vary according to the different groups, and the lack of agreement creates conflicts which permeate not only philosophical discussions but also the day-to-day relations of men and women.

Thus there is nothing in our lives, not even on the level of basic habits such as food, manners, behaviour, about which our views are not at variance. We do not even agree as to whether this great variety of opinions is good or bad, whether the greater conformity of the past or the modern emphasis on choice is to be preferred.

There is, however, one last issue about which we are clear. It is definitely not good to live in a society whose norms are unsettled and develop in an unsteady way. We realize this even more now that we are at war, when we must act quickly and without hesitation and fight an enemy whose value system is deliberately simplified in order to achieve quick decisions. In peace-time it might have been stimulating for the historian and the individual thinker to study the great variety of possible responses to the same stimulus and the prevailing struggle between different standards and differences in outlook. But, even in peace-time, this variety in valuations tended to become unbearable, especially in marginal situations where a simple "yes" or "no" was required. In such situations, many a man faced with the slowness of democracies in making their decisions came to share the view of a well-known Fascist political scientist who said that a bad decision is better than no decision. This is true to the extent that the indecision of the laissez-faire system represents a drifting which automatically prepares the ground for the coming dictator. Thus, long before the outbreak of war a few far-sighted thinkers became aware of the dangers inherent in the crisis in valuations, and tried to find the deeper causes of that crisis.

II. Controversy about the Causes of Our Spiritual Crisis

The two chief antagonists in the controversy about the causes of our spiritual crisis are the Idealists and the Marxists. To religious thinkers and philosophical idealists it seemed clear from the outset that the crisis in valuations was not the effect but rather the cause of the crisis of our civilization. To them all the struggles of history were due to the clash between different forms of allegiance to authority or to changing valuations. The abandonment of Christian and then of humanitarian valuations by modern man is the final cause of our crisis, and unless we restore spiritual unity our civilization is bound to perish. To the Marxist the exact opposite is true. What is happening in the world at present is nothing but a transition from one economic system to another and the crisis in values is, as it were, the noise made by the clash of these systems.

If you are a Liberal, your advice is to free the economic order from State interference with markets and let things of the spirit take care of themselves. If you are a Marxist, you see ideologies and valuations as a part of the social process, but in your strategy you too often focus your attack alone upon the economic aspects of society and hope that after the establishment of the right economic order a world of harmony will automatically emerge by the very action of dialectical interdependence. As the source of all our discord is to be sought in the antagonisms inherent in the Capitalist system, it is only natural that its removal will put everything right.

I think it was the great merit of the Marxist approach, as compared with the purely idealistic one, that it realized once for all that the life of culture and the sphere of valuations within it depend on the existence of certain social conditions, among which the nature of the economic order and of the corresponding class structure is of primary importance. This opened up a field of investigation which we call the sociology of culture. On the other hand, the exclusive emphasis on the economic foundations limited from the outset the outlook of the emerging sociology of culture. In my view, there are many other social factors and conditions upon which the life of culture depends, and the vocabulary of a sociology which approaches the crisis of culture with categories of "class" only is far too limited, as is the view that economic and class factors alone are responsible for the crisis in our valuations.

The difference in outlook will become explicit when we consider the remedy which follows from the two sociological approaches, the Marxist and that which I am to expound. According to the Marxist, you have only to put your economic house in order and the present chaos in valuation will disappear. In my view, no remedy of the chaos is possible without a sound economic order, but this is by no means enough, as there are a great many other social conditions which influence the process of value creation and dissemination, each of which has to be considered on its own merits.

In my sociological approach, as in the Marxist's, it is futile to discuss values in the abstract; their study must be linked up with the social process. To us values express themselves first in terms of choices made by individuals: by preferring this to that I evaluate things. But values do not only exist in the subjective setting as choices made by individuals; they occur also as objective norms, i.e. as advice: do this rather than that. In that case they are mostly set up by society to serve as traffic lights in the regulation of human behaviour and conduct. The main function of these objective norms is to make the members of a society act and behave in a way which somehow fits into the pattern of an existing order. Owing to this dual origin, valuations are partly the expression of subjective strivings, partly the fulfilment of objective social functions. Thus there is a continuous adjustment at work between what individuals would like to do if their choices were directed by their personal wishes only, and what society wants them to do.

As long as the structure of society is simple and static, established valuations will last for a very long time, but if society changes this will immediately be reflected in the changing valuations. Re-valuations and re-definitions of the situation will necessarily accompany the changed structure of society. A new social order cannot exist without these re-valuations and re-definitions, as it is through them alone that individuals will act in a new way and respond to new stimuli. Thus the valuation process is not simply an epiphenomenon superstructure, an addition to the economic order, but an aspect of social change in all its provinces where changed behaviour is wanted. But if valuations in their most important functions act as social controls, like traffic lights, it is obvious that we cannot bring order and harmony into the chaos of these controls unless we know a little more of the social processes which make these controls work, and about those social conditions which may upset the working of that signal system.

There is definitely a coherent system of social and psychological activities which constitute the process of valuation; among them value creation, value dissemination, value reconciliation, value standardization, value assimilation are the most important, and there are definite social conditions which favour or upset the smooth working of the process of valuation.

And this is exactly my contention. There has been a complete displacement of the social factors on which the smooth working of the process of valuation depended. But we have been so society-blind that we could not even properly distinguish these factors, let alone put right what went wrong. What I am going to do, therefore, is to try to enumerate some of those changed social conditions which upset the traditional functioning of the main factors in the process of valuations.

III. Some Sociological Factors Upsetting the Process of Valuation in Modern Society

(1) The first set of disturbances in the sphere of valuations arises from the simple fact of the uncontrolled and rapid growth of society. We pass from a stage where the so-called primary groups, family, neighbourhood, form the background to one where the larger contact groups prevail. As C. H. Cooley has pointed out, there is a corresponding transition from primary attitudes and virtues to derivative group ideals. The primary virtues of love, mutual help, brotherhood are deeply emotional and personal, and it is quite impossible to apply them without adjustment to the setting of larger contact groups. It is possible to love your neighbour whom you know personally, but it is an impossible demand to love people of a wider area whom you do not even know. In Cooley's view it is the paradox of Christianity that it tried to apply the virtues of a society based upon neighbourly relationships to the world at large. It did not only ask you to love the members of your tribe (a demand by no means peculiar to Christian-

ity), but also to love the whole of mankind. The solution to the paradox is that the commandment "Love your neighbour" should not be taken literally but should be translated according to the conditions of a great society. This consists in setting up institutions embodying some abstract principle which corresponds to the primary virtue of sympathy and brotherliness. The equal political rights of citizens in a democracy are abstract equivalents of the concrete primary virtues of sympathy and brotherliness.

In this case it is the method of translation which makes the value system function once more. But only social workers could tell us how often people fail in life because they never have been taught how to translate the virtues in which they have been trained in their homes into the conditions of society at large. To educate for family life and neighbourhood functions is different from educating for national and world citizenship. Our whole educational tradition and value system is still adapted to the needs of a parochial world, and yet we wonder that people fail when they are expected to act on a broader plane.

(2) Whereas in this case the method of translation helped to give meaning to primary virtues in a world of widening contacts, in other cases values of the neighbourly world will only function adequately under modern conditions if they are linked up with complete reform. Take, for example, the whole system of valuations which is linked up with the idea of private property. This was a creative and just device in a society of small peasants or small independent craftsmen, for, as Professor Tawney has pointed out, in this case the law of property only meant the protection of the tools of the man who did socially useful work. The meaning of the norm completely changes in a world of large-scale industrial techniques. Here the very same principle of the private ownership of the means of production implies the right to the exploitation of the many by the few.

This example shows from another aspect how, through the transition from simpler conditions to more complex ones, the very same rule, i.e. that of private property, may change its meaning completely, and may grow from an instrument of social justice into one of oppression. It is not enough to give a conscious reinterpretation of the value system organized around the idea of property; a complete reform is needed if the original intention, that the value of social justice should prevail, is to be put into practice again.

(3) The transition from a pre-industrial world where handicrafts and agriculture prevailed is not only reflected in the changing meaning of the valuations, which are focussed in the property concept, but also in a changing set of aesthetic valuations and of values regulating

our habits of work and leisure. It would not be at all difficult to demonstrate how in our appreciation of art the real struggle lies between the attitudes which are rooted in good craftsmanship and values which emanate from machine-made goods.

But the antagonism of values exists even more conspicuously in valuations which are linked up with the labour process. The working incentives and rewards of the pre-industrial age are different from those of our age. The prestige of the various occupations in a society of hand-made goods is different from the forms of prestige which emerge in the hierarchy of the factory and the business organization. New forms of individual and collective responsibility emerge, but very often the lack of opportunity for taking responsibility depresses those who still strive for self-respect through the skill invested in their work. It has rightly been said that our society has not yet assimilated the machine. We have successfully developed a new type of "taylorized" efficiency which makes man part of the mechanical process and moulds his habits in the interests of the machine. But we have not yet succeeded in creating those human conditions and social relationships in the factory which would satisfy the value aspirations of modern man and contribute to the formation of his personality.

The same applies to our machine-made leisure. The wireless, the gramophone and the cinema are now tools for producing and distributing new patterns of leisure. They are democratic in nature and bring new stimuli into the life of the humblest, but few of them have yet developed those genuine values which would humanize and spiritualize the time spent outside the workshop, factory and office.

Thus the machine age has either been incapable of producing adequate new values which would shape the process of work and leisure, or else is incapable of reconciling two different sets of competing ideals, both of which in their antagonism tend to disintegrate human character instead of integrating it. The same effect is visible in most of modern man's activities, as whatever he does in one compartment of his life remains unrelated to the others.

(4) Confusion in the sphere of valuation arises not only out of the transition from the conditions of the past to those of the present, but also through the growing number of contacts between groups. Through the growth in the means of communication and through social mobility such as migration or the rise and fall in the social scale, values of different areas are dropped into the same melting-pot. Formerly one could refer to different value areas: habits, customs and valuations of one county differed from those of another, or the scale of valuations in the members of the aristocracy differed from that of the

burghers. If groups made contact or even fused, there was time for assimilating one another's values; a kind of incorporation took place, and differences did not remain unreconciled nor survive as antagonistic stimuli. To-day we embody the most heterogeneous influences in our value system, and there is no technique for mediation between antagonistic valuations nor time for real assimilation. Against this background it becomes clear that in the past there were slow and unconscious processes at work, which carried out the most important functions of value mediation, value assimilation and value standardization. These processes are now either displaced or find neither time nor opportunity to do their work properly. This in itself reduces the value experience to insignificance. If a dynamic society is to work at all it needs a variety of responses to the changing environment, but if the variety of accepted patterns becomes too great it leads to nervous irritation, uncertainty and fear. It becomes gradually more and more difficult for the individual to live in a shapeless society in which even in the simplest situations he has to choose between various patterns of action and valuations without sanction; and he has never been taught how to choose or to stand on his own feet.

To counteract the ill-effects of this variety one would have to find some method of a gradual standardization of basic valuations in order to regain balanced attitudes and judgments. As this is lacking in our mass society, it is to be feared that out of the uncertainty there will emerge the cry for dictated values.

(5) Another source of displacement and disturbance in our value system is due to the entirely new forms of authority and sanctions which have emerged, and to the new methods of justifying existing authority and sanctions. When society was more homogeneous the religious and political authorities coincided at many points, or else there was a violent conflict to define the spheres of the religious and political authorities. But now we are faced with a variety of religious denominations and the disagreement between various political philosophies which, as all of them act at the same time, only succeed in neutralizing each other's influence upon the minds of the people.

Added to this we have the different methods of justifying authority. At one time there were only two ways of justifying the authority of social regulations: either they were a part of tradition ("as our forefathers have done it") or they expressed the will of God. Against this, the new method of value justification grew up, which acknowledged as its one source of acceptance that which could be deduced from eternal rational law, supposedly common to the human race. When this belief in enlightenment by the Universal Ratio as lawgiving power disintegrated, the door was thrown open to value justification of the most various kinds. The Utilitarian justification of values by their usefulness or the belief in the uncontrollable inspiration of the Leader became as plausible as the belief in the law of the strongest. Whether the latter finds expression in the theory of an eternal struggle between races, classes or élites is not of primary importance. In all these cases there is no end to the process of mutual extinction, as the justification is such as to admit endless arbitrary claims: why should not my leader have the vision, my race or class the vocation, to rule the world?

Another difficulty of the same order is that of focussing responsibility on some visible social agent. Where there is no acknowledged value system authority is dispersed, methods of justification become arbitrary and nobody is responsible. The focussing of authority and the allotment of different grades of responsibility to different functionaries are pre-conditions of the functioning of social life. But this focussing becomes more difficult as different classes, with their varying historical origins and mental make-up, adhere to different standards and as no attempt is made to reconcile their differences.

(6) An even worse predicament of our age is caused by the fact that whereas the most important values governing a society based upon the rule of custom were blindly accepted, the creation of the specifically new values and their acceptance is to a large extent based upon conscious and rational value appreciation. Whether one should love one's neighbour and hate one's enemy is based, as we have seen, upon the belief that this is either a demand of God or a part of our ancient traditions, but whether the democratic organization is preferable to the dictatorial one, or whether our educational system should pay more attention to the study of classics or to further specialization, these are decisions which have to be argued. Even if we agree that finally the preference might rest upon some irrational decision, persuasion has to go through the stage of conscious deliberation, and new techniques of conscious value appreciation are continually in the making.

Although this process leading to greater consciousness and deliberation is in itself a great advance, yet when it is brought into the existing social context it completely upsets the balance between conscious and unconscious forces operating in our society. The change to conscious value appreciation and acceptance is a Copernicus-like change on the social plane and in man's history, and it can only lead to improvements if it is really assimilated by society at large. To bear the burden of a greater amount of consciousness is only possible if many other things (among them education) are changed at the same time. The origins of this upsetting novelty are to be found in those days when man for the first time realized that through the conscious direction of law he could somehow influence a changing society. He thereby realized that it was possible to link up value creation and value guidance with conscious deliberation, to foresee and to some extent influence social effects. What is happening now is that what is already a matter of course in the legal sphere is being transferred to other spheres. In the spheres of education, pastoral work and social work, values of a moral rather than a legal nature are being linked up with rational deliberation and appreciation. Thus value creation, value dissemination, value acceptance and assimilation become more and more the concern of the conscious ego.

(7) This change is formidable, as in order to create a law-abiding citizen whose obedience is not solely based upon blind acceptance and habit, we ought to re-educate the whole man. People who are conditioned to accept values blindly either through obedience, imitation or emotional suggestion will hardly be able to cope with those values that appeal to reason and whose underlying principles can and must be argued. We have hardly realized yet, to its full extent, what a tremendous reform of education would be necessary to make a democratic society, based upon conscious value appreciation, function. There is one thing every reformer and educationist ought to bear in mind, and that is, that every new system of social controls requires the re-education of the self. In a society where the value controls were traffic lights directly appealing either to conditioned responses or to the emotions and the unconscious mind, one could bring about social action without strengthening the intellectual powers of the ego. But in a society in which the main changes are to be brought about through collective deliberation, and in which re-valuations should be based upon intellectual insight and consent, a completely new system of education would be necessary, one which would focus its main energies on the development of our intellectual powers and bring about a frame of mind which can bear the burden of scepticism and which does not panic when many of the thought habits are doomed to vanish.

On the other hand, if our present-day democracy comes to the conclusion that this frame of mind is undesirable, or that it is impracticable or not yet feasible where great masses are concerned, we ought to have the courage to build this fact into our educational strategy. In this case we ought, in certain spheres, to admit and foster those values which appeal directly to the emotions and irrational powers in man, and at the same time to concentrate our efforts on education for rational insight where this is already within our reach. It is possible to follow both courses: to train completely for irrational values in a society which is based upon them, or to train for rational deliberation where the values are such as to allow a great deal of rational justification on utilitarian grounds, for instance. But what is destined to lead to chaos is a clash between the nature of predominant valuations and the existing methods of education. You cannot create a new moral world mainly based upon rational value appreciation, i.e. values whose social and psychological function is intelligible, and at the same time maintain an educational system which in its essential techniques works through the creation of inhibitions and tries to prevent the growth of judgment. The solution seems to me to lie in a kind of gradualism in education, which acknowledges stages of training where both the irrational approach and the rational find their proper place. There was something of that vision in the planned system of the Catholic Church, which tried to present the truth to the simple man through images and the dramatic processes of ritual, and invited the educated to face the very same truth on the level of theological argument. There is no need to emphasize the fact that my reference to the Catholic Church is not to be interpreted as a recommendation of her dogma, but as an example showing how educational policy might be planned in a way that takes into account different types of value reception.

(8) We have seen some of the social causes making for crisis in our laissez-faire societies. We have seen how the transition from primary groups to great society, the transition from handicrafts to large-scale industrial techniques, the contacts between formerly separated value areas, caused disturbances in the process of valuation. We have seen how the new forms of authority and sanctions, the new methods of justifying authority, the lack in the focussing of responsibility and the failure to educate for conscious value appreciation, each by itself and all of them together contribute to the present crisis in valuations. We have finally seen how all the mechanisms which used to regulate automatically the process of valuation have gradually been weakened or eliminated without being replaced by anything else. It is no wonder, therefore, that our society lacks that healthy background of commonly accepted values and everything that lends spiritual consistency to a social system. If there is any truth in the Aristotelian statement that political stability depends on the adaptation of education to the form of government, if at least we agree with those who realize that a society can only function when there is a certain harmony of prevailing

valuations, institutions and education,—then our laissez-faire system is bound sooner or later to disintegrate.

In a society where disintegration has proceeded too far, the paradoxical situation arises that education, social work and propaganda, notwithstanding highly improved techniques, become less and less efficient because all the values that could guide them tend to evaporate. What is the use of developing exceedingly skilful methods of propaganda and suggestion, new techniques of learning and habit-making, of conditioning, de-conditioning and re-conditioning, if we do not know what they are for? What is the good of developing child guidance, psychiatric social work and psychotherapy if the one who is to guide is left without standards? Sooner or later everyone becomes neurotic, as it gradually becomes impossible to make a reasonable choice in the chaos of competing and unreconciled valuations. Only those who have seen the result of complete non-interference with valuations and deliberate avoidance of any discussion of common aims in our neutralized democracies, such as Republican Germany, will understand that this absolute neglect leads to drifting and prepares the ground for submission and dictatorship. Nobody can expect a human being to live in complete uncertainty and with unlimited choice. Neither the human body nor the human mind can bear endless variety. There must be a sphere where basic conformity and continuity prevail.

Of course, if we complain that our liberal and democratic system is left without a focus, we certainly do not want a regimented culture and an authoritarian education in the spirit of the totalitarian systems. But there must be something, a third way, between totalitarian regimentation on the one hand and the complete disintegration of the value system at the stage of laissez-faire on the other. The third way is what I call the democratic pattern of planning or planning for freedom. It consists essentially in the reverse of a dictatorial imposition of external controls. Its method is either to find new ways to free the genuine and spontaneous social controls from the disintegrating effects of mass society, or else to invent new techniques which perform the function of democratic self-regulation on a higher plane of awareness and purposeful organization.

By now it must have become obvious why I dwelt so long on the analysis of the main changes that have effected the working of the various factors in the process of valuations. One will also understand why I tried to enumerate some of the remedies, the techniques of readjustment in the process of valuations as, for instance, translation of values, creation of new values, complete reform, value assimilation, value standardization, value reconciliation, focussing of authority and responsibility, training in conscious value appreciation, etc. As the democratic planning of the value system will not consist in the inculcation of values, the careful study of the factors which make the spontaneous value process work in all its aspects in everyday life becomes an urgent task.

If we agree that real planning is democratic planning, then it follows that the problem is not whether we should plan or no, but to find the real difference between dictatorial and democratic planning. The development of the method of democratic value guidance, as it is gradually being worked out in the Anglo-Saxon democracies, and which, I hope, will be worked out even more in the future, is outside my scope here. I can only state some of the principles by which such a democratic form of value policy could be guided.

3 / THE IMPACT OF THE ELECTRONICS REVOLUTION
The Prospects of Automation

Computers and automation have a less visible impact on the lives of most of us than do many forms of technology. But their impact is already very great and is growing rapidly. Computers and their use to control the production of goods, commonly referred to as automation, have already freed millions of human beings from less-skilled labor and many forms of drudgery. It now seems realistic to expect, if human beings wish, that computers will someday take over all menial forms of human labor. In addition, computers and automation have made human labor far more productive, and indications are that we have only seen the beginnings of this increase in productivity. It is this increase in productivity which, coupled with new sources of energy derived from the control of nuclear fission and perhaps, someday, nuclear fusion, now promises great increases in abundance. Computers and automation have become the basic force creating the so-called "affluent society."

Freeing men from labor, and giving them far greater affluence, both have great impact on our values. Up until the last few decades, all societies in human history have been based on the assumption that goods are necessarily scarce and human labor is necessary to produce those scarce goods. Indeed, until recently, we have assumed that most men would have to be involved in a lifetime of "back-breaking labor" to fulfill our basic economic needs. As industrialization and now automation have increasingly belied these assumptions, many of the basic beliefs and values underlying our common patterns of everyday life have been undermined.

Millions of Americans have already felt the impact, both on their everyday lives and their values, of computers and automation through the increased leisure and affluence they bring about. Many certainly have experienced this with a sense of joy. They have felt freer and have felt a great increase in the things they can do in life. But it seems likely that many more have felt an uneasiness and perhaps anguish at no longer having their everyday lives constrained by the demands of labor and scarcity.

In the first essay in this section, David Riesman examines some of the many possible consequences of the computer age and automation for the values of American society. Not only does he see these new forces undermining the old work ethic of Protestant society, and potentially undermining all humanistic values, but he suggests as well that Aldous Huxley and others may have been right in fearing that the application of technology to production might free the masses from labor, but would at the same time place a greater burden of intellectual work on those who make and control the electronic machines. Moreover, he suggests that they might well be right in their fears that a "new class" of technocrats would arise to rule the new society. (This is a serious question which will be examined in the next part, "The Impact of Social Technology.")

The other essay in this section deals with the serious question of whether automation, or cybernation, might someday lead to the subjection of the human being to the machine. Norbert Wiener, one of the most important men in the early stages of the cybernetics revolution, and the author of the book *Cybernetics,* tries to show in his carefully reasoned argument that machines can eventually learn to do new things—things they have not been programmed by their builders to do. This theory forms the basis for his fears that machines might someday dominate their builders. He argues that we must reexamine our ancient value assumption that we should move ahead with the application of new knowledge as fast as possible. Otherwise, he argues, it may soon be too late for us to save ourselves from enslavement by machines.

Certainly we cannot be sure that the argument by Wiener is right. It may well be, as men such as Arthur Samuel have argued, that Wiener has overstated the capacity of machines to learn and perform original tasks. But there can be no doubt that this is a very serious question that we must examine for its possible effects on our fundamental value commitments to human freedom.

David Riesman

LEISURE AND WORK
IN POSTINDUSTRIAL SOCIETY

To the rest of the world, the American has characteristically appeared as someone who cannot stand being idle or alone, someone who rushes about, whether in work or play, and is preternaturally restless. Tocqueville for instance observed, "No men are less addicted to reverie than the citizens of a democracy." [1] Like Tocqueville, Lewis Mumford, in his remarkable book, *The Transformations of Man,*[2] discusses these changes from Old World to New World life, suggesting that the Americans, released by social and geographic space from age-old limits and norms, have exhibited from the beginning an exuberance and vitality, a romantic strenuousness, that in their respective ways Emerson and Whitman represented and celebrated.

I

At the present time, two processes are going on simultaneously. On the one hand, a decline of exuberance is just barely noticeable in America, making itself felt particularly among the more highly edu-

1. *Democracy in America,* Phillips Bradley edition (New York: Knopf, 1945), vol. 2, p. 208. Tocqueville had in mind the contrast with the members of an aristocratic society who had a smaller portion of discontent because people knew their place and, whether resignedly or not, remained in it; his view anticipated that of Durkheim.
2. New York: Harper, 1956.

cated and the well-to-do in a loss of appetite for work and perhaps even for leisure. On the other hand, the spread of industrialization and of the mass media are bringing both the residual pockets of traditionalism within this country and the great areas of it outside into a more "American" pattern. Whatever a nation's political or religious ideology, mass culture continues to spread, even ahead of industrialization, bringing the disruption of old ways and the lure of a new hedonism (as most dramatically seen in the cargo cults of the Pacific islanders which combine a nativist revival with the belief that the white man's goods can be obtained, without the white man himself, by appropriate rituals[3]).

I recently saw a documentary film focused on a family living in the hills of Tennessee in the 1930s—a family with many children and many dogs, eking out a bare existence. Despite efforts to insure minimal schooling, knowledge of the outside world scarcely percolated. Today, many of the very Tennessee shacks where, before the coming of the TVA, life resembled that in other peasant and pre-industrial cultures, are equipped with television aerials that now bring in not only the local boys who made good with a guitar, like Elvis Presley, but all the insignia of making good which pass as currency in the nation at large: cars, clothes, washers (which are often put on the front porch), and general styles of life and leisure. Some of the farms even in this area have become nearly as overmechanized, and hence engaged in "conspicuous production," as in the richer agricultural areas of the North; horses and mules are disappearing, and the South is catching up with the rest of the country in per capita ownership of automobiles.

Indeed, Southerners coming North, white or Negro, Caribbean or native, have replaced the immigrants from Southern Europe as fodder, not for the machines of production so much as for those of consumption; for coming from a pre-industrial culture they lack sales resistance, let alone consumer sophistication: entering, if not the high-wage economy, at least the high-credit one, they are being "processed" as consumers, while escaping, because of their late arrival, some of the drill and exhausting hours that met earlier pre-industrial cadres entering the work force of industrial society.

They enter a society which has over the past eighty years taken in the form of leisure or free time approximately a third of the gains in productivity which industrialism and organization have achieved. (The average work week now hovers around forty hours, as contrasted with

3. Cf., e.g., Margaret Mead, *New Lives for Old* (New York: William Morrow, 1955); also Daniel Lerner, *The Passing of Traditional Society* (Glencoe, Ill.: The Free Press, 1958).

seventy hours in 1850 and, in many industries and on the farms, nearly as much as that as late as 1920.) When the Bantu who works, let us say, in Johannesburg, has attained an increment over his old standard of living, he is likely to quit and return to the reservation; few of these Americans have a reservation to return to;[4] consequently, the Americans remain rather steadily at work while having time enough left on their hands for learning how to spend money in accordance with, and just beyond, their new wages. (There still remain in America more or less permanently underprivileged enclaves, principally among the old, the infirm, and among the less agile and mobile Negroes and poor whites.)

Those who have recently been released from underprivilege by mass production and mass leisure have gained, along with an often meaningless political vote, an often influential voice in the direction of consumption and hence of production. It is, for instance, the very millions whom Henry Ford helped release from drudgery who eventually defeated his ascetic and still rural canons of taste; it is they who like borax furniture or jukebox culture; their aesthetic is akin to that of all deracinated peasants whose folk culture crumbles at the first exposure to mass-produced commodities.[5]

4. To be sure, something analogous to a reservation exists in our urban and rural slums to which migrants come and in which they seek, despite pressures and temptations, to preserve enclaves of traditionalism. Conversely, even in Africa, the reservation, though geographically more stable, proves fragile in the face of the inducements and pressures of industrialism and urbanization.

5. The consequences of this overexposure, in the short and in the long run, are complex and are the themes of passionate debate (cf. the contributions to *Mass Culture* and especially Clement Greenberg's article, "Work and Leisure under Industrialism" in that volume). While I agree with Lyman Bryson that it is not right to judge a culture by its peaks of art and artisanship alone but that one must also judge it in terms of the total quality of its life [cf. *The Next America* (New York: Harper, 1950)], Bryson is readier than I to sacrifice the peaks of aristocratic attainment to the plateaus of popular contentment, in part because perhaps we differ on how long the latter can last without the former.

Certainly, the role of the artist changes when his patrons are no longer the few but the many. In a traditional society with a small elite, he is ancillary to the elite: they patronize him and he serves them, and he may remain unaffected by the attitudes and desires of the mass of the people—save as these furnish folk themes for his music or imagery. Even if patronized, he moves among those who count, whereas today the successful artist may be rich and famous and still not feel he knows anybody who counts. Artists and intellectuals in our time have a choice of constituencies: they may try to serve the traditional elite of culture and taste or the mass of people who for the first time in history have money enough to become patrons. This dilemma has driven some artists toward willful efforts to stave off mass understanding, whether by obscurities, sadism directed toward the audience, or serious attitudes which are unpopular. The results of this have not always been

II

As many thoughtful people have recognized, our society offers little in the way of re-education for those who have been torn away from their traditional culture and suddenly exposed to all the blandishments of mass culture—even the churches which follow the hillbillies to the city often make use of the same "hard sell" that the advertisers and politicians do. In the past, the relatively voluntary nature of the immigration to this country, and the belief in progress of natives and immigrants alike, have tended to blind us to the casualties of transplantation. There are a few exceptions. For example, in the 1930s I admired the Rust brothers, inventors of the cotton picker, who hesitated to market their invention because they were worried about technological unemployment among southern workers. (They were as unconvinced of the gospel of automatic technological progress as were the members of the Advisory Committee which recommended under Oppenheimer's leadership against proceeding with the H-bomb.) It is ironical to reflect that this invention came along just in time to save some southern fields from utter desertion—not only because Negroes and poor whites were leaving for the cities in the North but also because the cotton-picking machine, as a form of conspicuous production, frees its operator from work which has long been considered dirty work and thus raises the status of the operator: it is the counterpart

---

bad for art—on the contrary—but they do curtail some of the possibilities for the artist by making obscurities sometimes seem attractive per se. Conversely, such artists as, let us say, the typical jazz musician who plays popular, feel that they have sold out to the largest purse; the same occurs with painters who go commercial. Sometimes artists are thrown back upon their fellow artists as the only ones who understand this dilemma, but this does not always save an artist from being caught in the enormous machinery for disseminating his work if it catches hold. Indeed, if popular taste were utterly debased, than what is "high" and "low" could be clearly differentiated; but we have a situation of an infinite series of minute gradations in which it is not easy to say what is high-brow and upper-middle-brow and so on; thus, the Book-of-the-Month Club may circulate a very good book at times. As a result, the climate for the most intensive achievements of art and intellect has a good deal of smog in it: the artist does not necessarily starve but may be all too well patronized without giving him any sense that he has a genuine audience. Moreover, in an age of plenty, it may require more conviction for an artist to remain poor than when all but a few were poor. (I have profited from the discussion of these issues in Nathan Glazer's, "Technology, Mass Culture, and High Culture," a paper delivered at the American Sociological Society meetings, August 1958.)

on the production side of today's Tennessee shack, electrified and gadget-filled. Even so, I think that the Rusts' scruples were well taken people should not be ruthlessly torn away even from their incapacities and given the industrial bends: this country is rich enough and inventive enough to make social provision for a moratorium and retraining in those instances where uprooting is inescapable.

For many people today, the sudden onrush of leisure is a version of technological unemployment: their education has not prepared them for it and the creation of new wants at their expense moves faster than their ability to order and assimilate these wants.[6]

III

In the mercantilist era, and even today in the countries of grinding poverty, the creation of new wants has been a first step toward a better life and wider horizons of choice. But in the United States today, the belief that one cannot stop invention, cannot stop technological progress, has itself become a tradition, indeed a form of realistic insanity, or what C. Wright Mills calls "crackpot realism." Although adult Americans, contrary to European impression, are not dazzled by machines as such—but simply want to have those appurtenances that betoken an appropriate style of life—we are nevertheless half-willing slaves of the machine process. Even big business, thanks to the antitrust laws and to the potential competition of small business, does not quite have sufficient control of the market to plan to its own liking the sequence of applied technology. A fortiori, it seems inconceivable to Americans that we could reduce the aggression our technology keeps up against our traditions and the texture of our lives—

6. Since the writing of this paper, John Kenneth Galbraith's *The Affluent Society* (Boston: Houghton Mifflin Company, 1958) has appeared. With superb understanding, Professor Galbraith shows how the fear of economic insecurity which haunts Americans makes us the victims of our own productive processes—processes which create and then supply the "wants" as well as the leisure we choose because we don't want the wants that much. Galbraith also shows that the very primacy given to full production and full employment in the United States robs the economy of the flexibility that would permit diverting some of the surplus to wiping out the residual but stubborn poverty in this country and to making a dent on the vast and apparently increasing poverty of the nonindustrialized world. And Galbraith sketches some of the political and ideological reasons why high production has become a goal, not only for dairy cows, but for human beings—a goal which is now shared by liberals and conservatives and, almost by definition, by economists.

and we can always use the competition of the Russians to counter any tendency within ourselves to relax the rate of growth or to question the belief in growth as a value per se.

To be sure, the optimism of the booster was once much stronger in America than it is now. The ideal of Manifest Destiny, which took us across the continent and held the South bound to the Union in the Civil War, infects now only those perpetually adolescent males who are eager to conquer space or the planet Venus.[7] But the booster psychology has for so long been built into our culture and into our patterns of individual and group achievement that we tend to take for granted the notion that growth in population, in assets, in national income, is inevitable if not always desirable. Imagine the outcry, for instance, and not only from Catholics, against any suggestion that people be encouraged in this country to practice birth control, let us say, by removing the tax concession for child dependents or by instituting a sales tax on children's toys and clothes, or even by pointing out forcefully to people some of the less happy consequences of an exploding population.[8] For most Americans still believe that the future can take care of itself, or at any rate that we are not required to do anything to make it easier, less crowded, less full of friction, for our descendants.

In other words, we have become a conservative country, despite our world-wide reputation for seeking novelty, in that we are unable to envisage alternative futures for ourselves.

IV

So, too, it has been until recent years in the field of leisure time—so much so that my collaborators and I in *The Lonely Crowd* took it for granted that it was impossible to reverse the trend toward automation; we assumed that the current efforts to make work more meaningful— which by and large succeeded only in making it more time-consuming and gregarious but not more challenging—might as well be given up,

7. The space age is not a safety valve for the luxury economy and for our over-flowing energies. Although the comparison is often made, I believe there is a real difference between our space age and the exploration of this continent in the fifteenth and sixteenth centuries; at that time Europe was cramped and bound in all kinds of traditional constraints, and could find in colonization an opening for its growing population, its growing energies, its growing rationalism; the best use of the space frontier today would be to deflect our weapons—we can bombard Venus rather than each other.

8. For a better grasp of some of these problems, I am indebted to the writings of John R. Platt, Harrison Brown, and Richard L. Meier.

with the meaning of life to be sought henceforth in the creative use of leisure. We failed to see, in the famous Marxist phrase, that "quantity changes into quality" and that there would come a point where additional increments of leisure would prove more stultifying than satisfying and that the mass of men would be incapable of absorbing any more.

In pre-industrial cultures leisure is scarcely a burden or a "problem" because it is built into the ritual and ground plan of life for which people are conditioned in childhood; often they possess a relatively timeless attitude toward events. Likewise, the tiny leisure classes of the past would sometimes be able to absorb what seems like an overdose of leisure because they lived in an era when work itself was thought demeaning and when free citizens engaged in physical and intellectual self-cultivation and in the arts of war and government—they, so to speak, exercised their leisure on behalf of the whole society. During this era, which lasted throughout most of history, it was inconceivable that the mass of men could support a large and growing leisure class, let alone join such a class themselves. Yet today we live in such a world. The rich and leisured are no longer drastically set apart, but seek for the sake of their souls as well as their public relations to work with relative sobriety and consume with relative modesty and inconspicuousness; thus, they no longer set an example for either good or ill.[9]

At the present time, the closest thing we have to the traditional ideology of the leisure class is a group of artists and intellectuals who regard their work as play and their play as work. For such people, and for the larger group of professional people whom we shall discuss later, work frequently provides the central focus of life without necessarily being compartmentalized from the rest of life either by its drudgery and severity or by its precariousness. . . .

V

An informal poll of a union local (conducted by James Carper) found that the leaders did want a shorter work week whereas the rank and file did not. This was interpreted as suggesting that the leaders, better

---

9. It is however a very different story when one views the rich, not in their individual capacity, but in their collective capacity, whether corporate or national. For discussion of America's wealth as a barrier in our relations with other nations, see my Introduction to Daniel Lerner's book, *op. cit.*, and "Human Relations and National Boundaries," *Comprendre*, 1958.

educated and more enterprising, feel cramped for time to do everything they want to—to read more books, to see more of their families, to take more adult education courses. Such men already had many hobbies, including being union leaders. But the less active members (no doubt including many who might tell the union leaders that they "lack time to go to meetings") had no similar feeling of wanting the days to be longer. Such men, asked what they would do with an extra day, sometimes say, "sleep"; others could use it in hunting season—and already did so, to the dismay of the foreman. . . .

In a study by Nancy Morse and Robert Weiss, some 80 per cent of industrial workers stated that they, in effect, kept on working for lack of alternatives, not for positive satisfactions. These workers were asked whether they would go on working even if there were no financial need to do so, and they said they would, although also indicating that the job itself (and in many cases any job they could imagine) was boring and without meaning in its own terms. This clinging to the job is not simply a legacy of the Puritan ethic: it is rather a legacy of industrialism itself, of the old structures it has destroyed and the new structures it has created. Nor is it merely the feeling of shame in not having a job that is involved (although this is certainly an element). Work may not be an active presence in the life of American workers, but its absence would be an active absence. Or, more accurately, it is not so much *work* that would be missed as having a job: it doesn't have to be, and should preferably not be, hard work, nor need it even be gregarious work, but rather the self-definition (these data refer only to male workers) that comes from holding a job and the punctuations of life provided by regular employment. These workers, in other words, are too intelligent and too well educated to accept the routine of most factory work, while being still a long way away from the education of the artist or intellectual who can in some measure create his own work with a minimum of outside structuring.[10]

10. Many of the workers in the Morse-Weiss study harbor the vague hope of some day having a small business of their own, such as a gas station or television-repair shop. So too the practice of moonlighting or holding two jobs testifies not only to the continuing inflation of consumer wants and of the corresponding prices, but also to the fact that many factory workers are like the Russian peasants who were drafted into the collective farms: they give a minimum quantum of their work to the factory as the peasants did to the farms, and save up their real energies for the "private plots" of their work outside. Cf. Ely Chinoy, *Automobile Workers and the American Dream* (New York: Doubleday, 1955), and Charles R. Walker and Robert H. Guest, *The Man on the Assembly Line* (Cambridge, Mass.: Harvard University Press, 1952).

Such considerations concerning the limits of leisure suggest that it might be easier to make leisure more meaningful if one at the same time could make work more demanding. When work itself is infiltrated with leisure (as it is today in many jobs where the time-study man has been stymied), leisure may lose its savor, often becoming not much more than a continuation outside the plant of the sociability and inanity that go on within the plant. In this situation, I believe that we cannot take advantage of what remains of our pre-industrial heritage to make leisure more creative, individually and socially, if work is not creative too. And not only have we lost the folk and peasant traditions: we are rapidly losing those which have developed under industrialism itself—whether of the John Henry variety or of the free-swearing, free-swinging construction engineer who gets roads and dams built: such legends hold little allure in an opulent society, even when building continues at a rapid pace. It is from the Soviet Union that the story comes of a mill foreman who, though complaining of his pay, says he "must be content with the 'thrill of producing something anyway.' " [11] Though he may have been speaking in part for the record, there is no doubt that production remains exciting for many where industrialism is the unfinished business of a rising power. Americans, however, cannot artificially recreate that atmosphere; we cannot make factory or other industrial and commercial work over on the model of army basic training or campcraft just to make it hard (though in fact many workers do enjoy making a game of output, for instance, working up the line on an assembly line, in order to establish control and dramatize their activity). One alternative is to redesign our factories with an eye to the educational or challenging quality of each job, following the example set by some industrial units which have eliminated assembly lines and are giving workers larger units to assemble, or what is sometimes termed job enlargement. The march of specialization, which had originally been based on steam production but has in our day become an end in itself with its own dynamic and momentum, could thereby be reversed.[12] Undoubtedly, work flows

11. See Max Frankel, the New York *Times*, September 21, 1957, p. 3, col. 1.

12. See, e.g., Peter Drucker, *Concept of the Corporation* (New York: Harper, 1946), and the brilliant discussion by Daniel Bell, *Work and Its Discontents: The Cult of Efficiency in America* (Boston: Beacon Press, 1956).

To be sure, there would always be a question whether the work was being complicated only by the energy of the work force to create a plot for the daily drama of life or because the total configuration had been reorganized so that the work and the workers were seen as a single product. Assuredly, such reorganization, like anything else, could become a gimmick of management but it need not do so.

could be redesigned to maximize the demands on the worker's intelligence, while retaining present advances in making work quiet, free of dirt, and relatively unstrenuous. . . .[13]

VI

The hopes I had put on leisure (in *The Lonely Crowd*) reflect, I suppose, my despair about the possibility of making work in modern society more meaningful and more demanding for the mass of men—a need that has come upon us so rapidly that the taste of abundance we have had in the past now threatens to turn into a glut.

My despair on this score, I must add, was not greatly alleviated by the feeling in a group of union leaders in one of the more open-minded unions that it was impossible to get either unions or management in the least interested in making work more humanly satisfying. I hoped the union leaders might co-operate with management in, so to speak, turning the engineers around, and forcing them to design men back into their machines rather than out of them. As the discussion with the union officials continued, it became clearer to me that the workers themselves were too much of this same school of engineering thought really to believe in the reorganization of industry.[14]

13. Nelson Foote tells me of a case in Detroit some years ago where workers through their union insisted on their right to sing at work against the objections of a puritanical management. I am indebted to Mr. Foote, and particularly to his unpublished paper on "Stultification at Work," for illumination concerning the themes discussed in this paper.

14. It may be asked (and was) whether we can reverse our technical impetus and the trend toward automation without losing the very source of our leisure and our high productivity. In my opinion, we are already far past the point where we must be bound by such alternatives. In the great world of impoverished people with a very low life expectancy and the annual income of, let us say, an Indonesian villager, the question would answer itself: many people would be willing to sacrifice much for the greater amenity and ease of life Americans have. But if in America the changes I am recommending would make industry less productive, which I doubt, I think many of us would be willing to pay the price of working harder and having less so that we might have a more meaningful life at work. In fact, however, we have no evidence it would lower our over-all productivity to redesign our industrial pattern. Instead, I am convinced that ideology dominates factory and machine design to such an extent that we have a dream or myth of efficiency whose long-run cumulative costs are enormous in the sabotage and resentment of the work force, in boredom, in absenteeism, and so on. Engineers still act as if workers were as undisciplined and inefficient a group as they were before mass education and before industrialism—and by so doing they make our industry less productive than it might be even in its own terms.

In this perspective, the rebellion of workers against modern industry is usually mere rebellion, mere goofing off. Many are quite prepared to go on wildcat strikes (Daniel Bell notes that in 1954–55 there were forty such in just one Westinghouse plant in East Pittsburgh); they are quite prepared to deceive the time-study man and to catch forty winks on the night shift, and otherwise to sabotage full production while still "making out" in terms of the group's norms—being in this like students who might cheat on exams or cut classes but could not conceive of reorganization of the curriculum or of asking for heavier assignments. The great victory of modern industry is that even its victims, the bored workers, cannot imagine any other way of organizing work, now that the tradition of the early-nineteenth-century Luddites, who smashed machines, has disappeared with the general acceptance of progress. We must thus think of restriction of output and other sabotage of production as symtoms.[15]

Furthermore, the resentment that manifests itself in these symptoms helps engender a vicious circle, since it confirms the opinion of management that workers must be disciplined by bringing them together in great factories and subjecting them to the relentless pressure of assembly lines—as against the possibility, for instance, that work could be decentralized so that workers would not have to commute long distances and could proceed more at their own pace and place.[16] In the high-wage industries given over to "conspicuous production," management has the resources to be concerned with the amenities of work—the group harmony, the decor, the cafeteria and other ancillary services—and to make provision for the worker's leisure, such as bowling teams, golf courses, and adult education courses too; in fact, a whole range of extracurricular pleasures and benefits. Sometimes these benefits include profit-sharing, but they are much less likely to include decision-sharing, for of course managers object less to giving away money, especially money that would otherwise go to stockholders or to the government in taxes, than to giving away power and prestige and freedom of action to workers whose unionized demands reflect merely their discontent and scarcely at all any desires for reconstruction.[17]

15. For an understanding of how to look for and interpret such symptoms in a whole society or subculture, I am indebted to the work of Erich Fromm.

16. Cf. Daniel Bell, *Work and Its Discontents, supra;* also "The Evasion of Work" in *Work and the Welfare Age,* L.P.E. Papers no. 4, July 1956, pages 23–30.

17. What is General Motors to make, for instance, of some of the UAW locals' demands which are being presented in the current negotiations as these pages go to press, e.g., that the scores of World Series and other baseball games be announced at the end of each inning over the public address system or that motor scooters be

It is obvious in addition that managers are not free to reorganize their plants in order to provide their workers with a more satisfying work environment, if this might risk higher costs, unless their competitors are prepared to go along. Yet competition is not the whole story, for the situation is hardly better and is often worse in nationalized industries in Great Britain and Western Europe generally, while the situation of industrial workers in the Soviet Union today reminds one of the worst excesses of the Victorian era and the earlier days of the industrial revolution in the West. Managers of whatever ideological stripe seek to measure themselves against a single, unidimensional standard by which they can judge performance and thus are drawn to simplified work routines and an unremitting drive for maximum output. To open the possible consideration of factories as making not only things but also men, and as providing not only comfort and pay but also challenge and education, this would itself be a challenge to the way we have assimilated technology for the last three hundred years; and it would compel us to search for more Gestaltist and amorphous standards, in which we were no longer so clear as to what is process and what is product. There have, to be sure, been paternalistic employers (such as the Lowell mills in the 1840s or the Pullman plant a half century ago) concerned with the education and uplift of their operatives—often to the eventual resentment and unionization of the latter (who felt it was enough to have to work for the bosses without imitating their preferred inhibitions). But these were efforts to compensate outside the plant for the dehumanization regarded as inevitable within. What I am asking for now are explorations in reorganizing work itself so that man can live humanely on as well as off the job.

VII

The work of the managers themselves, of course, striving to get out production in the face of technical and human obstacles, is seldom boring, although if the product itself is socially valueless, a point may

---

furnished for union committeemen, or that workers be allowed to buy GM products at 40 per cent off! Another demand, that schedules be adjusted to allow employees wanting to go deer hunting to take time off (as in fact many do anyway), has a pre-industrial ring to it but hardly betokens a new rearrangement of work and leisure. See *Time*, June 9, 1958, page 84.

Lest I be misunderstood, let me make clear that I am not recommending arduousness per se, nor do I object at all to the steps workers and unions have taken to make life pleasanter and less exhausting.

be reached where work upon it, despite technical challenges, is felt as stultifying. Indeed, one could argue that the great disparities of privilege today are in the realm of the nature of work rather than in the nature of compensation: it has proved easier partially to equalize the latter through high-wage and tax policies than to begin at all on the former, which would require still greater readjustments. In that brilliant precursor of much contemporary science fiction, Aldous Huxley's *Brave New World,* the lower cadres are given over to fairly undiluted hedonism while serious work and thought are reserved for the ruling "Alphas." Likewise, a recent science-fiction story once more illuminates the issue (it is my impression that science fiction is almost the only genuinely subversive new literature in wide circulation today[18]): this is a story by Frederick Pohl called "The Midas Plague" which pictures a society in which the upper classes are privileged by being allowed to spend less time and zeal in enforced consumption; they are permitted to live in smaller houses and to keep busy fewer robots in performing services for them.[19] Their ration points—rations to extend rather than to limit consumption—are fewer; their cars are smaller; the things and gadgets that surround them are less oppressive. Best of all, they are allowed to work at work rather than having to spend four or five days a week simply as voracious consumers. That is, as one rises in the status system by excelling at consumership, one is allowed a larger and larger scope for what Veblen called the instinct of workmanship.

As already indicated, the world presented in "The Midas Plague," as in so much science fiction, is all too little a fiction. For, if we except a number of farmers and skilled workers, such as tool- and diemakers, it is the professional and executive groups who at present have the most demanding and interesting work and for whom, at least until retirement, leisure is least a time to kill. A survey by *Fortune* in 1957 showed that top executives, despite giving the appearance of being relaxed and of taking it easy as our mores demand, work an average of sixty hours a week or more. In many other fields, the leisure revolution has increased the demands on those who service the leisure of others or

18. Regrettably, few women appear to read science fiction and thus they fail to connect with a literature which at its best satirizes the additive and mechanistic quality of life; the world of technology remains a very "male" world and women rarely penetrate the technological fantasy to see the political fantasy which is on occasion at work underneath.

19. "The Midas Plague," in *The Case against Tomorrow* (New York: Ballantine Books, 1957). I am indebted to Eric Larrabee for a reference to this story and for conversations concerning matters touched on in this paper.

who have charge of keeping the economy and the society, or considerable segments of it, from falling apart. High civil servants and diplomats probably work as hard or harder than ever. The same is true of a good many teachers and professors who are presumably training others to spend their leisure wisely! . . .

In our egalitarian society, however, it would be surprising if the attitude of the masses did not influence the classes (there are of course also influences running the other way). As I remarked at the outset, I have the impression that a general decline is occurring in the zest for work, a decline which is affecting even those professional and intellectual groups whose complaint to their wives that they are overworked has often in the past been a way of concealing the fact that their work interested them rather more than did their wives. For example, there is some slight evidence that application lists to medical school are no longer so full, a decline which is attributed to the belief among young people that medical education is too arduous and takes too long before one is stabilized on a plateau of suburban life and domesticity. Similar tendencies would appear to be affecting those already in medical school. Howard S. Becker and Blanche Geer report (from the study of medical education at the University of Kansas being carried out under the direction of Professor Everett C. Hughes) that the teaching faculty complains that the students are no longer as interested in the more theoretical or scientific aspects of medicine: three quarters of them are married, and, instead of sitting around waiting for night duty or talking about their work, they are eager to go home, help the wife get dinner, and relax with television.

Likewise, there is evidence that young men in the big law firms, although they still work harder than most of their clients, do not glory in putting in night work and weekend hours as they once did. And several architects have told me that similar changes are showing up even in this field, which is famous for the enthusiasm of its devotees and the zest for work built up during *charettes* at architectural school. (Possibly, this may reflect in part the loss of the enthusiasm of the crusade on behalf of "modern" and the routinization of what had once been an esoteric creed.)

If such tendencies are showing up in the professions to which, in the past, men have been most devoted, it is not surprising that they should also be appearing in large-scale business enterprise. Though top executives may work as hard as ever—in part perhaps because, being trained in an earlier day, they can hardly help doing so—their subordinates are somewhat less work-minded. The recruiters who visit college campuses in order to sign up promising seniors or graduate students for large corporations have frequently noted that the students appear at least as interested in the fringe benefits as in the nature of the work itself; I would myself interpret this to signify that they have given up the notion that the work itself can be exciting and have an outlook which is not so very different from that of the typical labor-union member: they want and expect more but not so very much more than the latter.

The movement to the suburbs is of course a factor in these developments, especially now that young men move to the suburbs not only for the sake of their wives and young children and the latter's schooling but also for their own sake. It is hard, for example, for a scientific laboratory to maintain a nighttime climate of intense intellectual enthusiasm when its professional cadres are scattered over many suburbs and when the five-day week has become increasingly standard throughout American life (outside of a few universities which cling to the older five-and-a-half-day pattern). The sport-shirted relaxed suburban culture presents a standing reproach to the professional man who works at night and Saturdays instead of mowing the lawn, helping the Little League baseball team, and joining in neighborly low-pressure sociability. The suburbs continue the pattern of the fraternity house in making it hard for an individual to be a ratebuster or an isolate.

It is difficult to form a just estimate of the extent and scope of these changes. It is not new for the older generation to bewail the indolence of the young, and there is a tendency for the latter to maintain much of the older ethic screened by a new semantics and an altered ideology. Moreover, Americans in earlier periods were not uniformly work-minded. In Horace Greeley's account of his famous trip West in 1859 (which ended in his interviewing Brigham Young), he commented with disgust on the many squatters on Kansas homesteads who, in contrast to the industrious Mormons, sat around improvidently, building decent shelter neither for themselves nor for their stock (they sound a bit like Erskine Caldwell types).[20] Similarly, the correspondence of railroad managers in the last century (and railroad managers were perhaps the most professional managerial groups, as they were in charge of the largest enterprises) is full of complaints about the lack of labor discipline; this is one reason that the Chinese were brought in to work on the transcontinental roads. There were, it is evident, many backsliders in the earlier era from the all-pervading gospel of work, and the

20. Eric Hoffer has written that people who remember the "real" pioneers describe them in terms which resemble our picture of the Okies. "The Role of the Undesirables," *Harper's*, December 1952.

frontier, like many city slums, harbored a number of drifters.[21] Today, in contrast, the gospel of work is far less tenacious and overbearing, but at the same time the labor force as a whole is postindustrial in the sense of having lost much of its pre-industrial resistance to the clock and to factory discipline generally.[22]

VIII

So far, I have largely been discussing the uneven distribution of leisure in terms of differential attitudes toward work in different occupational groups. In comparison with the achievements of our occupational sociology, however, we have little comparable information concerning the sociology of leisure. For instance, we have very few inventories of how leisure is actually spent (apart from fairly complete information concerning exposure to the mass media). Pitirim Sorokin before World War II [23] and more recently Albert J. Reiss, Jr.,[24] have tried to get people to keep diaries which would include accounts of their day-by-day use of leisure time; but these suffer from faulty memory and stereotyping (people often say, "one day is just like another," and report

21. Even if proportionally there has been only a slight shift in the number of people who have no zest for work or shirk it, the social accent has shifted. It is clear from Leo Lowenthal's article on the change from heroes of production to heroes of consumption that even when men at work are pictured today in the mass media, what is emphasized is less their work than their golf score, their weekend behavior, their family life—and this emphasis must feed back to the men themselves and give them an image of how they ought to behave.

22. It would be interesting to know to what extent this change is a result of a general speeding up in the pace of life which seems to accompany urbanization and industrialization. I am told, for example, that the music of Bach and Mozart is played today some 10 per cent faster than the original tempo (the pitch is also higher). And it may be that the mass media, with their swift movement, help to expedite the rhythms of our contemporary life at work as well as at play. In this connection, Warner Bloomberg, Jr., has observed that factory workers in Gary sometimes have a hard time keeping their productivity down to the agreed-upon norms: they are apt to forget themselves and, without half trying, turn out too much (perhaps a little like the experience we may often have on a thruway of finding ourselves going faster than we had intended to). It would seem as if our society —in comparison with subsistence cultures—is geared to an interlacing of high-paced work and leisure; it gives that impression of speed-up still to visitors from abroad.

23. Pitirim A. Sorokin and Clarence Q. Berger, *Time-Budgets of Human Behavior* (Cambridge, Mass.: Harvard University Press, 1939).

24. Albert J. Reiss, Jr., "Rural-Urban and Social Status Differences in Interpersonal Contacts." Paper delivered at the American Sociological Society meetings, August 1958.

accordingly) as well as from omissions of fights and other improper activities. A more systematic study than most, by Alfred Clarke, found that radio and TV listening were the top two activities for both upper and lower prestige groups, followed by studying in the upper group and do-it-yourself activities in the lower.[25] The latter spend much more time just driving around, as well as polishing the car; they also spend much more time in taverns. Only in the upper group do people go out to parties, as against simply dropping in on a neighbor to look at TV or chat in the kitchen; and going to meetings is also largely confined to the upper group. In both groups, commercial recreation outside the home, such as going to the movies, plays little part. This and other, more impressionistic studies point to the conclusion that the busier people, the professionals and executives and better-educated groups generally, also lead a more active life in their time away from work; as the saying goes, they work hard and play hard. In Reiss's study, for example, there turned up a surgeon at a leading hospital who went to Mass every morning, then to the hospital, then to attend to his private practice; he belonged to about every community organization, and he and his wife entertained three or four nights a week. Contrastingly, at the other end of the social scale, the unemployed as we know from several studies have in a psychological sense no leisure time at all; they, and the underprivileged generally, do not belong to voluntary associations (churches and unions are an occasional exception); they live what is often a shorter life on a slower timetable.

At the same time, as I have indicated above, it is among the less privileged groups relatively new to leisure and consumption that the zest for possessions retains something of its pristine energy. Consumership which is complex if not jaded among the better-educated strata seems to be relatively unequivocal among those recently released from poverty and constriction of choice (although since the recession began, some of the latter may feel that they have been too ready victims for advertising and salesmanship and easy credit). With very little hope of making work more meaningful, these people look to their leisure time and consumership for the satisfactions and pride previously denied them by the social order. . . .

25. Alfred C. Clarke, "Leisure and Levels of Occupational Prestige," *American Sociological Review,* vol. 21 (1956), pp. 301–7; see also Robert J. Havighurst, "The Leisure Activities of the Middle-Aged," *American Journal of Sociology,* vol. 63 (1957), pp. 152–62.

IX

Even the most confident economists cannot adequately picture a society which could readily stow away the goods likely to descend upon us in the next fifteen years (assuming only a modest rise in annual productivity), with any really sizable drop in defense expenditures. People who are forced by the recession or by fear of their neighbors' envy or by their own misgivings to postpone for a year the purchase of a new car may discover that a new car every three years instead of every two is quite satisfactory. And once they have two cars, a swimming pool and a boat, and summer and winter vacations, what then?

Increasingly, as we all know, the motivation researchers are being pressed to answer these questions, and to discover what the public does not yet know that it "wants." Just as we are lowering our water table by ever-deeper artesian wells and in general digging ever deeper for other treasures of the earth, so we are sinking deeper and deeper wells into people in the hope of coming upon "motives" which can power the economy or some particular sector of it. I am suggesting that such digging, such forcing emotions to externalize themselves, cannot continue much longer without man running dry.

Even now, some of the surplus whose existence presents us with such questions is being absorbed in the very process of its creation by what I have termed the "conspicuous production" of our big corporations, acting as junior partners of the welfare state and absorbing all sorts of ancillary services for their own members and their own communities.[26]

Defense expenditures loom so large in our political as well as economic horizon because they do offer an easy and seemingly feasible way out by creating goods which do not themselves create other goods. (They are "multipliers" only in a Keynesian sense.) I would contend that expenditures which serve no real social imperative, other than propping up the economy or subduing the sibling rivalry of the armed services, will eventually produce wasteful by-products to slow that economy down in a tangle of vested inefficiencies, excessively conspicuous production, lowered work morale, and lack of purpose and genuine in-

26. As Professor Galbraith makes abundantly clear in his book (*supra*, note 6), these corporations along with their employees are actually senior partners, with the State and its subdivisions in contrast living shabbily as a very junior partner in a period of inflation. See *The Affluent Society*, ch. 14, 18, and elsewhere.

ventiveness.[27] The word "to soldier" means "to loaf" and conscription gives training in soldiering to a large proportion of the future work force (despite islands of asceticism in the Strategic Air Command or the air-borne "brushfire" infantry). For a time, men will go on producing because they have got the habit, but the habit is not contagious. Men will scarcely go on producing as mere items in a multiplier effect or conscripts in an endless cold war, nor will they greatly extend themselves to earn more money which they are increasingly bored with spending. To be sure, many workers have little objection to getting paid without earning it by traditional standards of effortfulness. And while those standards are usually irrelevant in a society of advanced technology and high expenditures on research and development, there are certainly many parts of the economy, notably in the service trades, whose gross inefficiency we only conceal from ourselves by contrasting America with pre-industrial societies or with those possessing far less adequate resources of men and machines—if we compare ourselves with the West Germans, for instance, or with the Canadians, the advance in our economy since 1946, great as it is in absolute terms, is unimpressive. The pockets of efficiency in our society are visible and made more so by the myth that we are efficient; hence, the evidence of disintegration and incompetence that is all around us strikes us as temporary or aberrant.

X

Correspondingly, some of our desires have been made highly visible by advertising and market research and lead to equally visible results such as good cars and, intermittently, good roads to drive them over.

27. Discussion-period question: "Isn't there a good deal of cynicism or debunking among workers concerning the product they are making?" Answer: "You are right that the problem of meaning in work lies not only in its intellectual or physical gamesmanship but in its relevance to the total social context. Thus, one could make work in an aircraft plant or missile plant more intriguing without in all dimensions making it more meaningful. Of course it does not prove that something is a good product because it gets bought. Cynicism among advertising men comes out of the feeling that the work they do, although creative in many ways—artistic, imaginative, ingenious in terms of research methods—is not meaningful or is actually harmful, so that they don't enjoy it. Surely this is the feeling of many intellectuals, whose work, although demanding and challenging, is not worthwhile. We must proceed on both fronts: to make the work more invigorating and pleasant in its own terms, that is, in terms of technical operations, and in terms of its bearing on what adds to human growth and development."

But other desires, which require co-operation to be effective, are often lamely organized and all but invisible. Thus, while some of us have a missionary zeal for learning, which we regard as the basis of later leisure as well as later employment, we have not been helped even by the push of sputnik to get a bill for school construction past the same Congress which eagerly voted federal money for highways (in part, no doubt, because the annual maintenance of schools falls upon a local tax base which grows constantly more inadequate while the maintenance of highways can be more easily financed from gasoline and registration taxes).[28] Other services, not so clearly "a good thing" as secondary and university education, are even more lacking in organized institutional forms which would permit the channeling of our surplus in ways which would improve the quality and texture of daily life. For example, even the great demand for scenic beauty (anemically reflected in the new highways) cannot make itself politically felt in preserving the country-side against roadside slums and metropolitan expansion, while men of wealth who could buy up whole counties and give them to the nation as a national park are lacking. It is extraordinary how little we have anticipated the problems of the bountiful future, other than to fall back on remedies which did not work in the less bountiful past, such as individualism, thrift, hard work, and enterprise on the one side, or harmony, togetherness, and friendliness on the other. Meanwhile, we stave off the fear of starvation in part by scanning the technological horizon for new goods that we will all learn to want, in part by the delaying tactic of a semiplanned recession, and, as already indicated, in part by the endless race of armaments.

That race has its cultural as well as Keynesian dynamic: as poll data show, a majority or large plurality of Americans expect war, though perhaps in a rather abstract way—war is one of those extrapolations from the past; like technological progress, we find it hard to resist. And, on the one hand, the threat of war is one factor in discouraging long-term plans, while, on the other hand, the continuation of the cold war provides a sort of alternative to planning. Thus, there tends to be a state of suspended animation in the discussion concerning the quality of life a rich society should strive for; social inventiveness tends to be channeled into the defense of past gains rather than into ideas for a better proportionality between leisure and work. Like soldiers off duty, "as you were," we subsist in default of more humane hopes.

But I should add that no other society has ever been in the same

28. On this point, as on so many others of this paper, Professor Galbraith's discussion adds clarity and perspective. See *The Affluent Society*, chs. 11, 13, 22, 25, and *passim*.

position as ours, of coming close to fulfilling the age-old dream of freedom from want, the dream of plenty. And I want to repeat that millions of Americans, perhaps still the great majority, find sufficient vitality in pursuit of that dream: the trip to the end of the consumer rainbow retains its magic for the previously deprived. Yet, by concentrating all energies on preserving freedom from want and pressing for consumer satiation at ever more opulent levels, we jeopardize this achievement in a world where there are many more poor nations than rich ones and in which there are many more desires, even among ourselves, for things other than abundance.

Norbert Wiener

SOME MORAL AND TECHNICAL CONSEQUENCES OF AUTOMATION

Some thirteen years ago, a book of mine was published by the name of *Cybernetics*. In it I discussed the problems of control and communication in the living organism and the machine. I made a considerable number of predictions about the development of controlled machines and about the corresponding techniques of automatization, which I foresaw as having important consequences affecting the society of the future. Now, thirteen years later, it seems appropriate to take stock of the present position with respect to both cybernetic technique and the social consequences of this technique.

Before commencing on the detail of these matters, I should like to mention a certain attitude of the man in the street toward cybernetics and automatization. This attitude needs a critical discussion, and in my opinion it should be rejected in its entirety. This is the assumption that machines cannot possess any degree of originality. This frequently takes the form of a statement that nothing can come out of the machine which has not been put into it. This is often interpreted as asserting that a machine which man made must remain continually subject to man, so that its operation is at any time open to human interference and to a change in policy. On the basis of such an attitude, many people have pooh-poohed the dangers of machine techniques, and they have flatly contradicted the early predictions of Samuel Butler that the machine might take over the control of mankind.

It is true that in the time of Samuel Butler the available machines were far less hazardous than machines are today, for they involved only power, not a certain degree of thinking and communication. However, the machine techniques of the present day have invaded the latter fields as well, so that the actual machine of today is very different from the image that Butler held, and we cannot transfer to these new devices the assumptions which seemed axiomatic a generation ago. I find myself facing a public which has formed its attitude toward the machine on the basis of an imperfect understanding of the structure and mode of operation of modern machines.

It is my thesis that machines can and do transcend some of the limitations of their designers, and that in doing so they may be both effective and dangerous. It may well be that in principle we cannot make any machine the elements of whose behavior we cannot comprehend sooner or later. This does not mean in any way that we shall be able to comprehend these elements in substantially less time than the time required for operation of the machine, or even within any given number of years or generations.

As is now generally admitted, over a limited range of operation, machines act far more rapidly than human beings and are far more precise in performing the details of their operations. This being the case, even when machines do not in any way transcend man's intelligence, they very well may, and often do, transcend man in the performance of tasks. An intelligent understanding of their mode of performance may be delayed until long after the task which they have been set has been completed.

This means that though machines are theoretically subject to human criticism, such criticism may be ineffective until long after it is relevant. To be effective in warding off disastrous consequences, our understanding of our manmade machines should in general develop *pari passu* with the performance of the machine. By the very slowness of our human actions, our effective control of our machines may be nullified. By the time we are able to react to information conveyed by our senses and stop the car we are driving, it may already have run head on into a wall.

Game-Playing

I shall come back to this point later in this article. For the present, let me discuss the technique of machines for a very specific purpose: that of playing games. In this matter I shall deal more particularly with the game of checkers, for which the International Business Machines Corporation has developed very effective game-playing machines.

Let me say once for all that we are not concerned here with the machines which operate on a perfect closed theory of the game they play. The game theory of von Neumann and Morgenstern may be suggestive as to the operation of actual game-playing machines, but it does not actually describe them,

In a game as complicated as checkers, if each player tries to choose his play in view of the best move his opponent can make, against the best response he can give, against the best response his opponent can give, and so on, he will have taken upon himself an impossible task. Not only is this humanly impossible but there is actually no reason to suppose that it is the best policy against the opponent by whom he is faced, whose limitations are equal to his own.

The von Neumann theory of games bears no very close relation to the theory by which game-playing machines operate. The latter corresponds much more closely to the methods of play used by expert but limited human chess players against other chess players. Such players depend on certain strategic evaluations, which are in essence not complete. While the von Neumann type of play is valid for games like ticktacktoe, with a complete theory, the very interest of chess and checkers lies in the fact that they do not possess a complete theory. Neither do war nor business competition nor any of the other forms of competitive activity in which we are really interested.

In a game like ticktacktoe, with a small number of moves, where each player is in a position to contemplate all possibilities and to establish a defense against the best possible moves of the other player, a complete theory of the von Neumann type is valid. In such a case, the game must inevitably end in a win for the first player, a win for the second player or a draw.

I question strongly whether this concept of the perfect game is a completely realistic one in the cases of actual, nontrivial games. Great generals like Napoleon and great admirals like Nelson have proceeded in a different manner. They have been aware not only of the limitations of their opponents in such matters as materiel and personnel but equally of their limitations in experience and in military know-how. It was by a realistic appraisal of the relative inexperience in naval operations of the continental powers as compared with the highly developed tactical and strategic competence of the British fleet that Nelson was able to display the boldness which pushed the continental forces off the seas. This he could not have done had he engaged in the long, relatively indecisive, and possibly losing, conflict to which his assumption of the best possible strategy on the part of his enemy would have doomed him.

In assessing not merely the materiel and personnel of his enemies but also the degree of judgment and the amount of skill in tactics and strategy to be expected of them, Nelson acted on the basis of their record in previous combats. Similarly, an important factor in Napoleon's conduct of his combat with the Austrians in Italy was his knowledge of the rigidity and mental limitations of Würmser.

This element of experience should receive adequate recognition in any realistic theory of games. It is quite legitimate for a chess player to play, not against an ideal, nonexisting, perfect antagonist, but rather against one whose habits he has been able to determine from the record. Thus, in the theory of games, at least two different intellectual efforts must be made. One is the short-term effort of playing with a determined policy for the individual game. The other is the examination of a record of many games. This record has been set by the player himself, by his opponent or even by players with whom he has not personally played. In terms of this record, he determines the relative advantages of different policies as proved over the past.

There is even a third stage of judgment required in a chess game. This is expressed at least in part by the length of the significant past. The development of theory in chess decreases the importance of games played at a different stage of the art. On the other hand, an astute chess theoretician may estimate in advance that a certain policy currently in fashion has become of little value, and that it may be best to return to earlier modes of play to anticipate the change in policy of the people whom he is likely to find as his opponents.

Thus, in determining policy in chess there are several different levels of consideration which correspond in a certain way to the different logical types of Bertrand Russell. There is the level of tactics, the level of strategy, the level of the general considerations which should have been weighed in determining this strategy, the level in which the length of the relevant past—the past within which these considerations may be valid—is taken into account, and so on. Each new level demands a study of a much larger past than the previous one.

I have compared these levels with the logical types of Russell concerning classes, classes of classes, classes of classes of classes and so on. It may be noted that Russell does not consider statements involving all types as significant. He brings out the futility of such questions as that concerning the barber who shaves all persons, and only those persons who do not shave themselves. Does he shave himself? On one type he does, on the next type he does not and so on indefinitely. All such questions involving an infinity of types may lead to unsolvable paradoxes. Similarly, the search for the best policy under all levels of sophistication is a futile one and must lead to nothing but confusion.

These considerations arise in the determination of policy by machines as well as in the determination of policy by persons. These are the questions which arise in the programming of programming. The lowest type of game-playing machine plays in terms of a certain rigid evaluation of plays. Quantities such as the value of pieces gained or lost, the command of the pieces, their mobility and so on can be given numerical weights on a certain empirical basis, and a weighting may be given on this basis to each next play conforming to the rules of the game. The play with the greatest weight may be chosen. Under these circumstances, the play of the machine will seem to its antagonist—who cannot help but evaluate the chess personality of the machine—a rigid one.

Learning Machines

The next step is for the machine to take into consideration not merely the moves as they occurred in the individual game but the record of games previously played. On this basis, the machine may stop from time to time, not to play but to consider what (linear or nonlinear) weighting of the factors which it has been given to consider would correspond best to won games as opposed to lost (or drawn) games. On this basis, it continues to play with a new weighting. Such a machine would seem to its human opponent to have a far less rigid game personality, and tricks which would defeat it at an earlier stage may now fail to deceive it.

The present level of these learning machines is that they play a fair amateur game at chess but that in checkers they can show a marked superiority to the player who has programmed them after from ten to twenty playing hours of working and indoctrination. They thus most definitely escape from the completely effective control of the man who has made them. Rigid as the repertory of factors may be which they are in a position to take into consideration, they do unquestionably—and so say those who have played with them—show originality, not merely in their tactics, which may be quite unforeseen, but even in the detailed weighting of their strategy.

As I have said, checker-playing machines which learn have developed to the point at which they can defeat the programmer. However, they appear still to have one weakness. This lies in the end game. Here the machines are somewhat clumsy in determining the best way to give the *coup de grâce*. This is due to the fact that the existing machines have for the most part adopted a program in which the identical strategy is carried out at each stage of the game. In view of the similarity of values of pieces in checkers, this is quite natural for a large part of the play but ceases to be perfectly relevant when the board is relatively empty and the main problem is that of moving into position rather than that of direct attack. Within the frame of the methods I have described it is quite possible to have a second exploration to determine what the policy should be after the number of pieces of the opponent is so reduced that these new considerations become paramount.

Chess-playing machines have not, so far, been brought to the degree of perfection of checker-playing machines, although, as I have said, they can most certainly play a respectable amateur game. Probably the reason for this is similar to the reason for their relative efficiency in the end game of checkers. In chess, not only is the end game quite different in its proper strategy from the mid game but the opening game is also. The difference between checkers and chess in this respect is that the initial play of the pieces in checkers is not very different in character from the play which arises in the mid game, while in chess, pieces at the beginning have an arrangement of exceptionally low mobility, so that the problem of deploying them from this position is particularly difficult. This is the reason why opening play and development form a special branch of chess theory.

There are various ways in which the machine can take cognizance of these well-known facts and explore a separate waiting strategy for the opening. This does not mean that the type of game theory which I have here discussed is not applicable to chess but merely that it requires much more consideration before we can make a machine that can play master chess. Some of my friends who are engaged in these problems believe that this goal will be achieved in from ten to twenty-five years. Not being a chess expert, I do not venture to make any such predictions on my own initiative.

It is quite in the cards that learning machines will be used to program the pushing of the button in a new push-button war. Here we are considering a field in which automata of a nonlearning character are probably already in use. It is quite out of the question to program these machines on the basis of an actual experience in real war. For one thing, a sufficient experience to give an adequate programming would probably see humanity already wiped out.

Moreover, the techniques of push-button war are bound to change so much that by the time an adequate experience could have been accumulated, the basis of the beginning would have radically changed. Therefore, the programming of such a learning machine would have to be based on some sort of war game, just as commanders and staff officials now learn an important part of the art of strategy in a similar manner. Here, however, if the rules for victory in a war game do not correspond to what we actually wish for our country, it is more than likely that such a machine may produce a policy which would win a nominal victory on points at the cost of every interest we have at heart, even that of national survival.

Man and Slave

The problem, and it is a moral problem, with which we are here faced is very close to one of the great problems of slavery. Let us grant that slavery is bad because it is cruel. It is, however, self-contradictory, and for a reason which is quite different. We wish a slave to be intelligent, to be able to assist us in the carrying out of our tasks. However, we also wish him to be subservient. Complete subservience and complete intelligence do not go together. How often in ancient times the clever Greek philosopher slave of a less intelligent Roman slaveholder must have dominated the actions of his master rather than obeyed his wishes! Similarly, if the machines become more and more efficient and operate at a higher and higher psychological level, the catastrophe foreseen by Butler of the dominance of the machine comes nearer and nearer.

The human brain is a far more efficient control apparatus than is the intelligent machine when we come to the higher areas of logic. It is a self-organizing system which depends on its capacity to modify itself into a new machine rather than on ironclad accuracy and speed in problem-solving. We have already made very successful machines of the lowest logical type, with a rigid policy. We are beginning to make machines of the second logical type, where the policy itself improves with learning. In the construction of operative machines, there is no specific foreseeable limit with respect to logical type, nor is it safe to make a pronouncement about the exact level at which the brain is superior to the machine. Yet for a long time at least there will always be some level at which the brain is better than the constructed machine, even though this level may shift upwards and upwards.

It may be seen that the result of a programming technique of automatization is to remove from the mind of the designer and operator an effective understanding of many of the stages by which the machine comes to its conclusions and of what the real tactical intentions of many of its operations may be. This is highly relevant to the problem of our being able to foresee undesired consequences outside the frame of the strategy of the game while the machine is still in action and while intervention on our part may prevent the occurrence of these consequences.

Here it is necessary to realize that human action is a feedback action. To avoid a disastrous consequence, it is not enough that some action on our part should be sufficient to change the course of the machine, because it is quite possible that we lack information on which to base consideration of such an action.

In neurophysiological language, ataxia can be quite as much of a deprivation as paralysis. A patient with locomotor ataxia may not suffer from any defect of his muscles or motor nerves, but if his muscles and tendons and organs do not tell him exactly what position he is in, and whether the tensions to which his organs are subjected will or will not lead to his falling, he will be unable to stand up. Similarly, when a machine constructed by us is capable of operating on its incoming data at a pace which we cannot keep, we may not know, until too late, when to turn it off. We all know the fable of the sorcerer's apprentice, in which the boy makes the broom carry water in his master's absence, so that it is on the point of drowning him when his master reappears. If the boy had had to seek a charm to stop the mischief in the *grimoires* of his master's library, he might have been drowned before he had discovered the relevant incantation. Similarly, if a bottle factory is programmed on the basis of maximum productivity, the owner may be made bankrupt by the enormous inventory of unsalable bottles manufactured before he learns he should have stopped production six months earlier.

The "Sorcerer's Apprentice" is only one of many tales based on the assumption that the agencies of magic are literal-minded. There is the story of the genie and the fisherman in the *Arabian Nights,* in which the fisherman breaks the seal of Solomon which has imprisoned the genie and finds the genie vowed to his own destruction; there is the tale of the "Monkey's Paw," by W. W. Jacobs, in which the sergeant major brings back from India a talisman which has the power to grant each of three people three wishes. Of the first recipient of this talisman we are told only that his third wish is for death. The sergeant major, the second person whose wishes are granted, finds his experiences too terrible to relate. His friend, who receives the talisman, wishes first for £200. Shortly thereafter, an official of the factory in which his son works comes to tell him that his son has been killed in the machinery and that, without any admission of responsibility, the company is sending him as consolation the sum of £200. His next wish is that his son should come back, and the ghost knocks at the door. His third wish is that the ghost should go away.

Disastrous results are to be expected not merely in the world of fairy tales but in the real world wherever two agencies essentially foreign to each other are coupled in the attempt to achieve a common purpose. If the communication between these two agencies as to the nature of this purpose is incomplete, it must only be expected that the results of this cooperation will be unsatisfactory. If we use, to achieve our purposes, a mechanical agency with whose operation we cannot efficiently interfere once we have started it, because the action is so fast and irrevocable that we have not the data to intervene before the action is complete, then we had better be quite sure that the purpose put into the machine is the purpose which we really desire and not merely a colorful imitation of it.

Time Scales

Up to this point I have been considering the quasi-moral problems caused by the simultaneous action of the machine and the human being in a joint enterprise. We have seen that one of the chief causes of the danger of disastrous consequences in the use of the learning machine is that man and machine operate on two distinct time scales, so that the machine is much faster than man and the two do not gear together without serious difficulties. Problems of the same sort arise whenever two control operators on very different time scales act together, irrespective of which system is the faster and which system is the slower. This leaves us the much more directly moral question: What are the moral problems when man as an individual operates in connection with the controlled process of a much slower time scale, such as a portion of political history or—our main subject of inquiry —the development of science?

Let it be noted that the development of science is a control and communication process for the long-term understanding and control of matter. In this process fifty years are as a day in the life of the individual. For this reason, the individual scientist must work as a part of a process whose time scale is so long that he himself can only contemplate a very limited sector of it. Here, too, communication between the two parts of a double machine is difficult and limited. Even when the individual believes that science contributes to the human ends which he has at heart, his belief needs a continual scanning and re-evaluation which is only partly possible. For the individual scientist, even the partial appraisal of this liaison between the man and the process requires an imaginative forward glance at history which is difficult, exacting and only limitedly achievable. And if we adhere simply to the creed of the scientist, that an incomplete knowledge of the world and of ourselves is better than no knowledge, we can still by no means always justify the naïve assumption that the faster we rush ahead to employ the new powers for action which are opened up to us, the better it will be. We must always exert the full strength of our imagination to examine where the full use of our new modalities may lead us.

4 / THE THREATS OF ALIENATION AND SOCIAL TECHNOLOGY

In this part we consider two of the more specific threats of the technology involved in our automated economy, those of the potential alienation of men from their work, or even their society, and the possible uses of the new forms of thought to impose a technological tyranny on men. The first essay in this part, by Daniel Bell, is concerned with what has traditionally been called the alienation of modern man. The alienation of modern man has been a theme common to the social sciences and the humanities since the nineteenth century, when many educated men became deeply concerned about the growing effects of industrialization on everyday life. Arguments about alienation have taken many different forms. In the nineteenth century, many social critics and sociologists alike argued that science, technology, and industry were increasingly eliminating the affective, or emotional, aspects of everyday life. They argued that these forces, especially the rationality of science, were destroying the ancient myths, religious beliefs, and other sources of emotional gratification that made everyday life endurable and enjoyable. They foresaw a complete secularization of thought, an end to the "holy," and the rise of chilling rationality and cold boredom in everyday life. More recent analyses have seen alienation in terms of meaninglessness, powerlessness, and a number of other factors. But they have all had in common the belief that in some way forces within the individual which are of vital necessity for his well-being and sense of gratification in life can no longer find adequate expression in the modern world.

Many of the earlier fears and beliefs about the alienation of modern man now seem to be false. While it is certainly true that traditional forms of religion have been increasingly secularized, or even eliminated, it is also true that there has been in recent years a great growth in the belief in ancient forms of magic and mystical thought. Moreover, it now appears clear that traditions of religious expression have merely given way to more private forms of expression, and certainly few would care to argue that modern man is less given to emotionalism than men of the nineteenth century. Surely the riots, ideological arguments, and killings in recent years would dispel any such illusion. In general, it would seem that the earlier beliefs that modern man suffers from an incurable alienation from society were inspired by fears of the great social changes being wrought by industrialization and the scientific-technological revolution in general. Modern men who have grown up in societies dominated by science, technology, and industry do not experience the same kind of alienation.

Nevertheless, there is still plenty of evidence of alienation. What Daniel Bell argues in this article is that the alienation takes different forms. In some ways, he feels that man's alienation today is more severe, more fundamental, than the alienation of nineteenth-century man. Because of this, some of his prognoses for modern man are even more bleak. He believes the alienation of modern man is due primarily to what he calls the disjunction of culture and social structure. Essentially, he argues that our social relations, or what he calls social structure, have become so immensely specialized and complex because of the continued development of science and technology that it is no longer possible for us to find an adequate shared symbolic expression, or what he calls culture, for our everyday lives. While he sees many other complicating factors also leading the disjunction of culture and social structure, he believes this is the dominant factor. In the final section of his article, he integrates his view of the alienation of modern man with a more traditional nineteenth-century view, arguing that modern thought is being increasingly mathematized, resulting in an increasing rationalization of thought.

While Bell's essay constitutes a very serious argument concerning the possible predicament of modern man, we must view it in the perspective of the earlier arguments about the alienation of nineteenth-century man. This argument, too, may be largely the result of the authors' having come from an earlier age and not being at home in the scientific and technological society. Moreover, it would seem clear that he has failed to see some of the growing countervailing forces in modern society, such as the growth in various forms of mysticism and magic. (His argument that these are merely escapes from the dominant mode of production may be right, but it is not yet clear that that is the case.) There are those who argue that science and technology, by freeing man from the humdrum existence of menial labor, liberates him for wholly new forms of life which he himself is free to choose, precisely because of his affluence and leisure time. I suspect we will not know for some time who exactly is right in this argument, but it is clear that the arguments presented by Bell deserve very careful attention.

The second selection in this part examines the possibilities that the rise of the technological society will not only produce a disjunction between social structure and culture, but that the growth of technological forms of thought about man, which Bell dealt with only briefly at the end of his work, might become the basis for a technological —or a social science.

Since the beginning of the social sciences, which goes back at least to the early part of the nineteenth century, social scientists and their supporters have had the control of human behavior in some form or another as one of their basic goals. Indeed, the basic stimulus for all the social sciences was probably a desire to understand, explain, predict, and thereby control social behavior for the betterment of everyone. The realization of this goal has been slow, perhaps simply because the social sciences, like most sciences, have developed slowly, but there are now very important ways in which the sciences of man and society are already able to control human behavior. And certainly every indication is that it will be even more possible to control human behavior in the years ahead.

The possibility that science can give men the power to control other men poses a fundamental challenge to our basic values of human freedom and democratic government. Indeed, as some people have argued, the increasing control over most segments of our society by technological experts makes the threat of expert control over our whole society by the social technocrats a very real one.

One of the foremost proponents of benevolent control by experts over human society has been B. F. Skinner. In his book *Walden Two,* Skinner outlined what he saw as a modern utopia created and run by those with expert scientific knowledge of human behavior. In the following article, "Some Issues Concerning the Control of Human Behavior," Skinner argues that all human beings are already involved in trying to understand, predict, and thereby control the behavior of other human beings. He maintains that he is simply trying to make this whole process more scientific and, therefore, more effective and better for everyone. But Skinner's ideas have aroused great controversy among the social scientists themselves. In his responses to Skinner's ideas in *The Symposium,* Carl Rogers, one of the foremost proponents of freedom among social scientists, argues that Skinner has not answered the basic criticisms of his views. He argues that there is certainly no way of guaranteeing that scientific controls over human behavior will be controlled by those who truly seek the best interests of all. Indeed, he argues that the prospects are that the men of power who would wield such controls would not be benevolent scientists seeking the happiness of everyone. Rogers argues on the contrary that social scientists should seek to help others by being nondirective rather than trying to control them. He argues that this is the only way we can truly make other people happier.

Daniel Bell

THE DISJUNCTION OF CULTURE
AND SOCIAL STRUCTURE
Some Notes on the Meaning of Social Reality

". . . social forces always find expression in culture, even when they work unseen, and the problem is stated falsely if culture and society are torn apart from one another and are regarded as fully independent spheres which, as such, react upon one another. The social process is contained in the very structure of cultural life itself so that it is never for one moment free from its influence."

Karl Mannheim—*Man and Society in an Age of Reconstruction*

The thesis of these notes is that one of the sources of our difficulty in comprehending contemporary "culture" (that is, giving it a stylistic definition other than the ambiguous term "modernity") is the disjunction between the social structure and the culture. By social structure I mean the system of social relationships between persons, institutionalized in norms and rules. By culture I mean the symbolic expressions in the realms of ideas and art of the experience of individuals in those relationships. The disjunction arises because of difficulties involved in finding appropriate symbolic expression for efforts to grasp the meaning of experiences in contemporary society.

In one sense, none of this is new. Man, seemingly, has had the recurrent feeling—call it alienation, forlornness or existentialist despair —of being lost, or cast out of the world. In Christian sensibility there is the agonized theme of the separateness of man from God. In the

"The Disjunction of Culture and Social Structure" by *Daniel Bell. From* Daedalus *(Winter 1965): 236–50. Reprinted by permission of Daedalus, Journal of the American Academy of Arts and Sciences. This essay was originally given as the Sigmund Falk Memorial Lecture at Hebrew Union College in Cincinnati on November 12, 1964.*

esthetic humanism of Schiller there is the lament that the "zoon condition" of Greek life, where man was a perfect whole, has given way to the differentiation of function, resulting in an estrangement of the intuitive and speculative minds and the dissociation of sensibility. In Hegel, there is the cosmic drama of the movement of the world from a pre-existent unity through the dualities of nature and history, thought and experience, man and spirit, to the re-unification of the Absolute in the "realization" of philosophy. For Marx, in a more naturalistic mode, it was the division of labor (of mental and physical labor, of town and country) which was generally responsible for alienation in work, plus the specific fact that in a commodity-exchange society a man becomes "reified" in his labor so that his personality becomes dissolved in his function.

Contemporary experience, in its effort to articulate its own disorientation, draws from all these speculative and philosophical reflections. But at times excessively so, for musings about "the human condition" only blur the distinctiveness of modern times or the distinctive ways in which some of these larger truths become expressed in concrete fashion. Yet modes of experience do vary radically in time and place. Lucien Febvre once pointed out that the age of Rabelais had little *visual* sense, that hearing in particular seemed to precede and remain more important than sight, a primacy which was reflected in the imagery of the prose and poetry of the time. Or Marcel Granet has attempted to show how particular conceptions of number (but not quantity), space and time played a distinct role in the formulation of classic Chinese political philosophy and classic Chinese art.

Contemporary social science, however, has tended to eschew this form of analysis. It deals with formal organizations or social processes (for example, industrialization) but rarely with the modes of experience themselves, modes which mediate between social structure and culture. These notes, an exploration in sociological analysis, seek to illustrate the ways in which social perceptions are shaped, often unconsciously, by modes of experience.

I. The Revolution in Sensibility

Our technical civilization is not only a revolution in production (and in communication); it is a revolution in sensibility as well. The distinctiveness of this civilization—call it "mass society" or "industrial society"—can be understood in a number of ways; I choose to define it (not exhaustively) within these dimensions: number, interaction, self-consciousness, and future-time orientation. In effect, the way in which we confront the world is conditioned by these elements.

Number. In 1789, when George Washington was inaugurated as the first president of the United States (and the Constitution had just been ratified), American society comprised fewer than four million persons, of whom 750,000 were Negroes. Few persons lived in cities; New York, then the capital, had a population of 33,000 persons. In all, 200,000 individuals lived in what was then defined as "urban areas"—meaning, places with more than 2500 inhabitants. It was a young population: the median age was sixteen, and there were only 800,000 males above that age.

Because it was a small country, members of the political elite knew each other, as did the thin stratum of leading families. But for most persons, living in isolated clumps or in sparsely inhabited areas, life was vastly different. People rarely traveled great distances; a visitor from afar was a rarity. News meant local gossip, and the few news sheets concentrated on parochial events. The ordinary person's image of the world and its politics was extremely limited.

Today, the United States numbers well over 180,000,000 persons, more than a hundred million of whom live in metropolitan areas (that is, within a county containing at least one city of 50,000 residents). The median age is over thirty and 130,000,000 persons are over fourteen years of age. Few persons live or work in social isolation. Even those who work on the farms are tied to the national society by the mass media and the popular culture.

In the way in which we "perceive" the world today, as against 1789, two aspects are striking: the difference in the number of persons each of us *knows,* and the number each of us *knows of.* On the job, in school, in the neighborhood, in a profession, in a social milieu, an individual today knows literally hundreds if not thousands of other persons; and with the multiplication of the mass media—with the enlargement of the political world, and the enormous multiplication of entertainment figures and public personalities—the number of persons one *knows of* accelerates at a steeply increasing rate.

Simply, then, the number of encounters each of us has, and the range of names, events and knowledge we have to master—this is the most obvious fact about the world which today confronts us as a "given."

Interaction. The "mass society," however, is not composed of numbers alone. Czarist Russia and Imperial China were large landmass societies, with huge numbers of persons. But these societies were essentially segmented, each village largely recapitulating the features of the other. It was Emile Durkheim in his *Division of Labor* who gave us the clue to what is distinctive about the mass society. It is when segmentation breaks down and people come into interaction with each other—where ensuing competition leads not necessarily to conflict but to more complex divisions of labor, of complementary relationships and of increased structural differentiation—that new social forms emerge.

What is distinctive, then, about contemporary society is not only its size and number, but the increased interaction—physical (through travel, through larger work units, through larger housing densities) and psychic (through the mass media)—which ties us to so many other persons, directly and symbolically. Increased interaction leads not only to social differentiations but as a mode of experience to psychic differentiation as well—to the desire for change and novelty, to the search for sensation, to the syncretism of culture, all of which mark so distinctively the rhythm of contemporary life.

Self-consciousness. To the classic question of identity, "who are you," a "traditional" person would say: "I am the son of my father." [1] A person today says, "I am I, I come out of myself, and in choice and action I make myself."

This change of identity is the hallmark of our own modernity. For us, experience—rather than tradition, authority, revealed utterance or even reason—has become the source of understanding and of identity. Experience is the great source of self-consciousness, the confrontation of self with diverse others.

Insofar as one makes one's *own* experience the touchstone of truth, one seeks out those with whom one has common experience in order to find common meanings. To this extent, the rise of generations, and the sense of generation, is the distinct focus of modern identity. [2] But

1. One sees this, of course, in the traditional Russian patronymic, or the usual Arab form of naming, such as Ali ben Achmed, or in the residues of old English names such as John/son, Thom/son, and the like.

2. In more traditional societies, or in the early phases of contemporary society, *social class* was usually the main source of identity. The rise and fall of families, as Schumpeter noted, was the rise and fall of social classes. In the earlier quest for position and power in society one sought to rise with one's class, or, as more open mobility became possible, to rise out of one's class (cf. Trilling's "Young Man from the Provinces"). Social class is still today a potent shaper of identity, but it decreases in importance with the rise of education as the chief route to "place" in society. Both in the literary sphere (where the process has a long history) and now in the political realm, the generation assumes a great importance. For the immigrant worlds—and America has been equally a land of many such worlds—the generation has been the chief source of psychic identity.

this change is, also, the source of an "identity crisis." The idea of reality, sociologically, is a fairly simple one. Reality is a confirmation by "significant others." Traditionally, a *bar-mitzvah* is a confirmation by the Jewish community, a marking out of a new status (the acceptance of the responsibility for the covenant) in a ceremonial act. Graduation from school is a confirmation in a new role and a new status. When a person is confirmed by others, there has to be some sign of recognition.

Reality breaks down when the confirming "others" have lost their meaning for the person seeking to locate himself or to find a place in the society. The sociological problem of reality in our time—in terms of social location and identity—arises because individuals have left old anchorages, no longer follow inherited ways, are constantly faced with the problems of choice (the ability to choose—to choose careers, styles of life, friends, political representatives—is, for the mass of people, something new in social history), and find no longer authoritative standards or critics to guide them. The change from family and class to generation as the "structural" source of confirmation thus creates new strains in identity.

Time-orientation. Ours is a society that has become "future-oriented" in all its dimensions: a government has to plan for future growth; a corporation has to plan for future needs (capital sources, market and product changes, etc.); the individual has to think in terms of a career. In effect, society no longer goes on in crescive fashion; it becomes mobilized for specific ends.

The greatest pressures today devolve upon the young person. At an early age he is under pressure to make firm choices; to get good grades in school, to enter a good college, to choose a vocation. At all stages he is rated, and the performance ratings now become a card of identity that he carries throughout his life.

The failure to provide adequate mechanisms during the transitional period (that is, school guidance, vocational counselling) leads to obvious strains—it invites "beat" behavior and other forms of opting out of the system. In this respect, the "beat fad" parallels the behavior of the early industrial worker when the machine harness was slipped over him as he came off the farm. In both instances one finds wild outbursts (the machine-breaking of the early industrial revolution is matched, perhaps, by drop-out rates in high schools and colleges), the pastoral romance (which in the case of the "beats" becomes slum romance), and similar forms of unorganized class struggle.

The new emphasis on the future in terms of social as well as individual planning—and the resistance to this emphasis because of the new kinds of pressures which such an emphasis entails—becomes a new dimension of our experience in American society.

These four elements, as I have sought to indicate, shape the way in which individuals respond to the world. Two of them—number and interaction—are features of the social environment which "structure" our responses, unconsciously, in the way in which the balancing of mass and size of type on the front-page of a newspaper tends to direct our eye in a determinate sequence. They are responsible, primarily, for the emphasis in modern sensibility on *immediacy, impact, novelty, sensation* and *simultaneity*. These rhythms also tend to shape (as I have sought to show in an essay in *Encounter*, May, 1963) the technical forms of painting, music and literature as well. The emergence of self-consciousness (or the "cult of experience") and the pressures of a mobilized society—particularly where the social mechanisms have been inadequate to handle the problems of innovation and adaptation—have led to the more open and conscious modes of ideological response to the society—to rebellion, alienation, retreatism, apathy or conformity,[3] modes that are sharply etched on the surface of the culture.

II. The Diremption of Culture

These modes of experience—together with some more formal aspects of industrial society, principally functional specialization, and the requirements of the new "intellectual technology"—are reflected in certain disjunctions between the social structure and the culture.

I single out for illustration three realms in which these disjunctions have occurred: 1) The disjunction of "role" and "person"; 2) Functional specialization: the disjunction between "role" and "symbolic expression"; 3) The change in vocabulary: from metaphor to mathematics.

1. THE DISJUNCTION OF ROLE AND PERSON

In contemporary sociology—as in the intellectual world as a whole—there rages a debate as to whether modern society is one of increasing depersonalization or of increasing freedom. It seems strange that views so diametrically opposite are held by intellectually re-

3. I am adopting here, for only slightly different purposes, Robert Merton's well-known paradigm in his essay "Social Structure and Anomie."

sponsible persons with little effort either to mediate, reconcile, or even establish the terms upon which the debate is conducted.

In a theoretical sense, the roots of the two positions (as expressed in modern sociology) go back contrastingly to Max Weber and Emile Durkheim. For Weber, the drift of society was one of increasing bureaucratization (or functional rationality) in which the greater specialization of function meant the increasing separation of the individual from the control over the enterprises of which he was a part.[4] Regulated by the norms of efficiency, calculability, and specialization, man is seen as an appendage to "the clattering process of the bureaucratic machinery."

Durkheim had an almost contrary perspective. In the way he dichotomized social change, the shift from "mechanical solidarity" was, in effect, a movement from homogeneity to heterogeneity, from uniformity to diversity. Societies of the first kind had little division of labor; the collective spirit was so strong that violations of rules were dealt with in a retributive way. Societies of the second type featured a complex division of labor, a separation of sacred from secular elements, a greater choice of occupations, and a loyalty to one's profession rather than to the parochial group as the source of identity or belonging. Sharing some elements of nineteenth-century evolutionary beliefs, though not the unilinearity of a Maine or a Spencer, Durkheim saw social development as inherently "progressive" in its unfolding, though precipitating new kinds of problems. (In one sense, the emphasis of a Weber is on *rationalization,* of a Durkheim on the *rational.*)

This bifurcation continues in contemporary sociology and in intellectual life generally. Those adhering to the Marxist or an existentialist position emphasize the depersonalization inherent in modern bureaucratic life—*vide,* Marcuse, Fromm, Tillich. Others, such as Talcott Parsons or Edward Shils, emphasize the way in which modern society allows for greater variety of choice, the emphasis on achievement, the up-grading of occupations and a greater individualism.

How does one thread one's way through this debate? As William James once said, whenever you meet a contradiction, make a distinction, for people often use the same words to mean two different things. In a curious way, both theories are correct, largely because each is

4. In Hans Gerth's formulation: "Marx's emphasis upon the wage worker as being 'separated' from the means of production becomes in Weber's perspective merely one special case of a universal trend. The modern soldier is equally 'separated' from the means of violence; the scientist from the means of enquiry, and the civil servant from the means of administration."

talking about a different dimension. If one makes the distinction between *roles* and *persons,* one can perhaps see the way each theory talks past the other.

I think it is quite evident, following Weber, that modern society increasingly forces a narrow specialization of roles. Broad aspects of life which were once centered in the family (namely, work, play, education, welfare, health) are increasingly taken over by specialized institutions (enterprises, schools, trade unions, social clubs, the state). Role definitions (the many different hats we wear) become sharper, and in the crucial area of work, where in the nineteenth-century *mythos* a man found his identity, tasks and roles become minutely specialized. (*The Dictionary of Occupational Titles* lists over 20,000 different specialized jobs in its analysis of vocational outlooks. We even see this in intellectual tasks. The National Register of Scientific and Specialized Personnel, in compiling lists of intellectual talents in the country, now lists about 900 fields in the sciences.)

Within organizations the creation of hierarchies, job specifications, minute definition of responsibilities, rating systems, escalator promotions, and the like, all give emphasis to this sense of fragmentation of self—as it is defined through the *role.*

At the same time it is also clear that, as a *person,* one now has a wider range and variety of choices than ever before. There are many more different kinds of jobs and professions. One can travel to many different places and live in different cities. In the area of consumption (and in using culture as a form of consumption), there is a wider provenance for creating a personal, or a chosen, style of life. All of this is summed up in the phrase, which is distinctive in its modern application, "social mobility."

Modern life creates a bifurcation of *role* and *person* which for a sentient individual becomes a strain.[5]

2. FUNCTIONAL SPECIALIZATION: THE DISJUNCTION OF ROLE AND SYMBOLIC EXPRESSION

A characteristic of science, as of almost all organized human activity, is the increasing segmentation, differentiation and specialization —sub-division and sub-specialization—of each field of knowledge.

5. This distinction between *role* and *person* is somewhat different from the distinction between *office* and *person.* Any society, in order to enforce authority, emphasizes a distinction (most notably in an army) between a *rank* and the person bearing the rank. One obeys the rank, not the person.

Natural philosophy, which was an inclusive term in the seventeenth century, sub-divided into the natural sciences of physics, chemistry, botany, zoology, and so forth. Speculative philosophy of the nineteenth century gave rise to sociology, psychology, mathematical logic, symbolic logic, analytical philosophy, and so forth. In any of the fields today, new problems give rise to further specializations: chemistry, which was once divided into analytical, organic, inorganic, and physical, is in one accounting sub-divided into carbohydrate, steroid, silicone, nuclear, petroleum, and solid state.

One sees this process not only in the fields of knowledge, but in the character of organizations, as new problems give rise to new functions and to new specializations to deal with them. Thus a business corporation which once had a simple staff-and-line organization now finds itself confounded with the problems of coordinating a dozen broad functions such as research, marketing, advertising, quality control, personnel, public relations, design, finance, production, let alone the dozens of sub-specializations within each of the functions (so that personnel, for example, would include labor relations, internal communications, job training, plant security, safety, time records, welfare and medical benefits, and the like). And one finds similar divisions in *every* formal organization, whether it be a business enterprise, a university, a hospital, or a governmental agency.

The point in all this is that the high degree of specialization—both in the fields of knowledge as well as in the structures of organizations—inevitably creates an almost unbearable strain between "the culture" and the social structure. In fact, it becomes quite difficult to speak even of "the" culture, for not only do specializations create "sub-cultures" or private worlds—in the anthropological sense—but these in turn create private languages and private signs and symbols which often (the case of the jazz musician is the most obvious) infiltrate the "public" world of culture.

Today, the culture can hardly, if at all, reflect the society in which people live. The system of social relations is so complex and differentiated, and experiences so specialized, complicated or incomprehensible, that it is difficult to find common symbols of meaning to relate one experience to another.

In the nineteenth century, the "agency" of expression was the novel. The function of fiction, paradoxically, was to report fact. When social classes began to confront each other in the nineteenth century in the comedy of manners and morals, there was great curiosity as to how each class lived, or as to how individuals who moved up the social ladders took on, or failed to take on, new class styles and modes. There was equally an interest in the nature of work.

The extraordinarily differentiated social structure which has come into being today makes it difficult for a novelist—and even a sociologist—to probe the nature of the worlds of work. Thus fiction, as well as social criticism, tends to deal with consumption styles, or reflect in the themes of alienation and bureaucratization the sentiment against the honeycomb complexity of social structure.

Insofar as experiences in the society are no longer generalizable into the culture, culture itself becomes private, and the individual arts either technical or hermetic. At the turn of the century, the function of the critic was to "mediate" between the creative new experiments being conducted in painting and music, and to find a common esthetic to explain them. Today there is no critic who can assimilate music to painting or painting to music—and it is probably not the fault of the critic. Even the arts have become highly technical: the "new criticism" in literature as a parallel to the technical innovations of the great novelist-masters; the complex intentions of abstract-expressionist painting, with its new emphasis on surface and space.

The real difficulties in the appreciation of the "modern" (both in literature and painting) have been masked by the fact that they have become modish, and, through their popularizers and imitators, common coin for the consumption culture. The only genuine avant-garde movement today is in music, and it remains so because the new electronic music, or post-Webern tonalities, or the new mathematics of serial music, are so technical that even a critic finds it difficult to act as intermediary to other arts, let alone the general public.

The rise of pop art, the introduction of "chance" elements in music, the appreciation of "junk" as esthetic, and the vogue of "happenings" in which paint, sculpture (posture), music and dance are fused into one, all reflect the reaction against the technical and hermetic elements in art. It is not only a new way to "shock" even a blasé public, but it poses a threat to the traditional (and formal) conceptions of genre in a new way. If John Dewey could say that "Art is Experience," what these practitioners are saying is that all "experience is Art." It is, in effect, a denial of specialization by an insistence on the fusion of all arts but one. It is an erasure of all boundaries between the arts, and between art and experience.

3. The Disjunction of Vocabulary: From Metaphor to Mathematics

Reality is always inferential (who has seen custom?) and we employ concepts to describe reality. In the history of "culture" one or another mode of experience has always been dominant as the source of concepts. It is the change in language—the expansion of the abstract mode of thought—which enlarges the disjunction of our experience.

In the primitive world-view—and in such sophisticated primitivism as Zen Buddhism—the world is presented in its immediacy. One did not say "hard" or "soft," for even these terms pre-suppose philosophical ontologies (for example, the nature of substance, or the problem of relative degree); something was "stone" rather than "hard," or "grass" rather than "soft."

Greek cosmogony gave us a vocabulary of first-level abstraction. The pre-Socratics introduced metaphor; Plato, with the idea of the demiurge, the symbol; Aristotle, the idea of analogy. (Our traditional modes of thought here employed all three. Imagery can be visual, aural or tactile, but employs the techniques of metaphor, symbol or analogy in "picturing" the world.)

Theological speech, as derived from Christian thought, is deeply soaked in symbols—the Cross, the Messiah, the Epiphanies, the Sacraments—and the language emphasizes mystery and personality: grace, charisma, kairos, passion or suffering, ritual.

The breakdown of theological beliefs and the rise of a scientific world-view, leading to the enthronement of physics and the natural sciences, gave us in the eighteenth and nineteenth centuries a mechanical cosmology—the image of the world as a machine, or as a celestial clock. (This ordered world reached its apogee in two images: the beauty and precision of Laplace's *Mécanique Céleste,* in which the universe functioned as a jewel, and the idea of the "great chain of being" in which all creatures were united in one perfect strand. In Alexander Pope's words: "Vast chain of Being! which from God began,/Natures ethereal, human, angel, man,/Beast, bird, fish, insect, what no eye can see,/No glass can reach, from Infinite to thee.")

The language of analysis, once derived from theology, was now wrested from the early physical sciences. (Poetry, driven, as Whitehead put it, from the world of fact by science, resorted to ambiguity as its mode of expression, while modern existentialist theology finds its mode in paradox.) In the social sciences the key terms were Force, Motion, Energy, Power (and while these terms have specific referents in physics, they have few operational specificities in social analysis). But as the natural sciences progressed, the social sciences added new biological analogies to the metaphors derived from physics: evolution, growth, organic structure and function, and these terms, until most recently, were the language of sociology.

Even when, in the nineteenth century, social science sought to find a language of its own—"economic man," "psychological man," "capitalism," etc.—this led to a conceptual realism or what Whitehead called "the fallacy of misplaced concreteness." The search for "a language of one's own" in order to avoid the trap of reification has led (as exemplified in Talcott Parsons' *Structure of Social Action*) to "analytical abstraction." Thus, theory construction in sociology, for one, has become a highly deductive system derived from a few basic axioms, or really analytical concepts such as the patterned variables in the action schema of Parsons, in which the empirical referents no longer stand for concrete entities (the individual, society, etc.).

But in the more general sweep of knowledge, the dominant mode of intellectual experience today is mathematical, and especially in our new "intellectual technology" (linear programming, decision theory, simulation) we have the "new" language of variables, parameters, models, stochastic processes, algorithms, hueristics, minimax, and other terms which are being adopted by the social sciences.

Yet the type of mathematics that is influential here is not the deterministic calculus of classical mechanics, but a calculus of probabilities. Life is a "game"—a game against nature, a game of man against man, and one follows rational strategies which can provide maximum pay-offs at maximum risks, minimax pay-offs at minimax risks, and that most lovely of terms in utility preference theory, a pay-off which is provided by a "criterion of regret."

But all of this leads to a paradox: the modern vocabulary is purely rational, with no referent other than its self-contained mathematical formulae. In a modern cosmology (as in physics, and now in the other sciences as well), pictures have gone, words have gone; what remains—apart from elegance, but the elegance of formal ingenuity—is abstract formulae. And underneath these formulae there is no law of nature as we knew it before, eternal, universal, immutable, and readily discernible. Underneath are uncertainty and the break-up of temporal and spatial sequence.[6]

6. Whether it is pure fancy or genuine speculation, it is interesting that a writer in the *Times Literary Supplement*, in commenting on the influence of computers on

Thus our vocabulary reinforces the dominance of an abstract world conception. And this is the penultimate disjunction between culture and social structure.

III. *The Eclipse of Distance*

The underlying social reality, the stylistic unity of the culture of the past hundred years, lies, I would argue—though its explication is far beyond the scope of this essay—in a structural form of expression that I have called "the eclipse of distance," of psychic, social and esthetic distance.[7] Modern culture began as an effort to annihilate the contemplative mode of experience by emphasizing *immediacy, impact, simultaneity,* and *sensation.* It is today at the point of breaking up all fixed points of reference in formal genres.

The esthetic intention, from the mid-sixteenth to the mid-nineteenth century, was to establish certain formal principles of art around the rational organization of space and time. The painting of the Renaissance—say the painting of Uccello—was "rational" in that it not only applied formal mathematical principles to the depiction of a scene, but also sought to translate into art a rational cosmography of space as depth and time as sequence. In music, as Max Weber pointed out, the diatonic scale was the basis for a rational organization of chords. The fundamental intention of the neo-classical critics, such as Lessing, was to set forth "laws" of esthetic perception: literature and painting, working through different sensuous media, differ in the fundamental laws governing their creation. But underneath all this was a notion of rational organization: depth, the projection of three-dimensional space, gave objects a time value, a simulation of the real world; narrative and sequence were chronological chains which provide a sense of progression.

The diverse movements of modern art have acted to break up this rational construction. Modern painting, eliminating interior distance, thrusts itself on the viewer, emphasizing a sense of immediacy and

---

the organization of knowledge, sees it as breaking up "linearity" (and introducing "simultaneity") in the organization of prose and in the production of effects. The discussion of this would take us, for the moment, far afield. (See "Poetry, Prose, and the Machine" in the *Times Literary Supplement,* May 4, 1962. This is reproduced in the pamphlet, published by the T. L. S., *Freeing the Mind.*)

7. I can provide only the barest outlines—and forgo the necessary examples and illustrations—of what the reader will recognize is a very complex argument. But this is a sketch, from a work in progress, and I leave it in chiaroscuro outline.

impact, seeking to capture a simultaneity of planes on a single canvas. Modern poetry, beginning with the theory of "verbal reckless-ness" as formulated by Rimbaud, breaks up fixed rules of syntax and grammar and, with Mallarmé, abandons referential brute reality to concentrate on the words themselves and their internal relationships within phrase and sentence. The modern novel becomes associative in thought, stream of consciousness in structure, phenomenological in its surfaces, and destructive of sequence and temporality. Modern music, taking Schoenberg as the turning point, denies the necessity of any structural harmonic background and becomes obsessed with sound alone. The remarkable fact is that in all the arts—painting, poetry, the novel, and music (and the cinema *par excellence*)—one can discern a *common* structure of expression, despite the conscious intentions of the artists. This common structure is the "eclipse of distance."

In the loss of "psychic distance," there is the suspension of time, a substitution of moment and event for sequence. In the modern novel, the consequence is to bring the "primary process," the dream sense, to the fore; and the spectator is pulled into the work. In the loss of "esthetic distance," the work "imposes" itself on the spectator; and one must respond, in one's feelings, immediately to the experience. At root, what this has meant is the overturning of the "rational cosmography"—the orderly sequence of time, of beginning, middle, and end; the interior conception of space, of foreground and background, of figure and ground—which shaped Western thought from the sixteenth to the mid-nineteenth century.

The search of the modern was a search for the heightening of experiences in all dimensions and to make those experiences immediate to the senses of people. Yet some cultural signs indicate that we may have come to the end of that phase, a movement which reached its apogee in the esthetic rebellion of 1890–1930. The aimlessness of Camus' *L'Étranger,* the anti-novels of Robbe-Grillet and Butor with their denial of introspection, the vogue of Zen, with its efforts to deny self-consciousness, the static, decaying worlds of Beckett, the hallucinogenic cults fostered by the drug-takers, all express a nihilism or a gnosticism which is subversive of society itself. The literature of modernity—the literature of Yeats, Lawrence, Joyce, and Kafka—was a literature which, as Lionel Trilling put it, took "to itself the dark power which certain aspects of religion once exercised over the human mind." But it was, in its private way, concerned with spiritual salvation. Its successors seem to have lost concern with salvation itself. In this sense, it has become "post-modern" or "post-Christian."

For Ortega y Gasset, art was the freest activity of the human imagination, the least dependent of human actions on social constraints and conditions; and, for this reason, the first signs of change in collective sensibility became noticeable there. The agonized fantasies of a Rimbaud a hundred years ago prefigure the cruder cult of adolescence today. But what does the anti-art of the post-modernist cults foreshadow for the morrow? In the disjunction of culture and social structure it is becoming increasingly more difficult to tell.

Carl R. Rogers and B. F. Skinner

SOME ISSUES CONCERNING THE
CONTROL OF HUMAN BEHAVIOR
A Symposium

SKINNER

Science is steadily increasing our power to influence, change, mold—in a word, control—human behavior. It has extended our "understanding" (whatever that may be) so that we deal more successfully with people in nonscientific ways, but it has also identified conditions or variables which can be used to predict and control behavior in a new, and increasingly rigorous, technology. The broad disciplines of government and economics offer examples of this, but there is special cogency in those contributions of anthropology, sociology, and psychology which deal with individual behavior. Carl Rogers has listed some of the achievements to date in a recent paper.[1]

Those of his examples which show or imply the control of the single organism are primarily due, as we should expect, to psychology. It is the experimental study of behavior which carries us beyond awkward or inaccessible "principles," "factors," and so on, to variables which can be directly manipulated.

It is also, and for more or less the same reasons, the conception of human behavior emerging from an experimental analysis which most directly challenges traditional views. Psychologists themselves often do not seem to be aware of how far they have moved in this direction. But the change is not passing unnoticed by others. Until only recently

"Some Issues Concerning the Control of Human Behavior: A Symposium" by Carl R. Rogers and B. F. Skinner. From Science *124 (November 30, 1956): 1057–66. Reprinted by permission of the authors and* Science.

1. C. R. Rogers, *Teachers College Record* 57, 316 (1956).

it was customary to deny the possibility of a rigorous science of human behavior by arguing, either that a lawful science was impossible because man was a free agent, or that merely statistical predictions would always leave room for personal freedom. But those who used to take this line have become most vociferous in expressing their alarm at the way these obstacles are being surmounted.

Now, the control of human behavior has always been unpopular. Any undisguised effort to control usually arouses emotional reactions. We hesitate to admit, even to ourselves, that we are engaged in control, and we may refuse to control, even when this would be helpful, for fear of criticism. Those who have explicitly avowed an interest in control have been roughly treated by history. Machiavelli is the great prototype. As Macaulay said of him, "Out of his surname they coined an epithet for a knave and out of his Christian name a synonym for the devil." There were obvious reasons. The control that Machiavelli analyzed and recommended, like most political control, used techniques that were aversive to the controllee. The threats and punishments of the bully, like those of the government operating on the same plan, are not designed—whatever their success—to endear themselves to those who are controlled. Even when the techniques themselves are not aversive, control is usually exercised for the selfish purposes of the controller and, hence, has indirectly punishing effects upon others.

Man's natural inclination to revolt against selfish control has been exploited to good purpose in what we call the philosophy and literature of democracy. The doctrine of the rights of man has been effective in arousing individuals to concerted action against governmental and religious tyranny. The literature which has had this effect has greatly extended the number of terms in our language which express reactions to the control of men. But the ubiquity and ease of expression of this attitude spells trouble for any science which may give birth to a powerful technology of behavior. Intelligent men and women, dominated by the humanistic philosophy of the past two centuries, cannot view with equanimity what Andrew Hacker has called "the specter of predictable man." [2] Even the statistical or actuarial prediction of human events, such as the number of fatalities to be expected on a holiday weekend, strikes many people as uncanny and evil, while the prediction and control of individual behavior is regarded as little less than the work of the devil. I am not so much concerned here with the political or economic consequences for psychology,

2. A. Hacker, *Antioch Rev.* 14, 195 (1954).

although research following certain channels may well suffer harmful effects. We ourselves, as intelligent men and women, and as exponents of Western thought, share these attitudes. They have already interfered with the free exercise of a scientific analysis, and their influence threatens to assume more serious proportions.

Three broad areas of human behavior supply good examples. The first of these—*personal control*—may be taken to include person-to-person relationships in the family, among friends, in social and work groups, and in counseling and psychotherapy. Other fields are *education* and *government*. A few examples from each will show how nonscientific preconceptions are affecting our current thinking about human behavior.

Personal Control

People living together in groups come to control one another with a technique which is not inappropriately called "ethical." When an individual behaves in a fashion acceptable to the group, he receives admiration, approval, affection, and many other reinforcements which increase the likelihood that he will continue to behave in that fashion. When his behavior is not acceptable, he is criticized, censured, blamed, or otherwise punished. In the first case the group calls him "good"; in the second, "bad." This practice is so thoroughly ingrained in our culture that we often fail to see that it is a technique of control. Yet we are almost always engaged in such control, even though the reinforcements and punishments are often subtle.

The practice of admiration is an important part of a culture, because behavior which is otherwise inclined to be weak can be set up and maintained with its help. The individual is especially likely to be praised, admired, or loved when he acts for the group in the face of great danger, for example, or sacrifices himself or his possessions, or submits to prolonged hardship, or suffers martyrdom. These actions are not admirable in any absolute sense, but they require admiration if they are to be strong. Similarly, we admire people who behave in original or exceptional ways, not because such behavior is itself admirable, but because we do not know how to encourage original or exceptional behavior in any other way. The group acclaims independent, unaided behavior in part because it is easier to reinforce than to help.

As long as this technique of control is misunderstood, we cannot judge correctly an environment in which there is less need for heroism, hardship, or independent action. We are likely to argue that such an environment is itself less admirable or produces less admirable people. In the old days, for example, young scholars often lived in undesirable quarters, ate unappetizing or inadequate food, performed unprofitable tasks for a living or to pay for necessary books and materials or publication. Older scholars and other members of the group offered compensating reinforcement in the form of approval and admiration for these sacrifices. When the modern graduate student receives a generous scholarship, enjoys good living conditions, and has his research and publication subsidized, the grounds for evaluation seem to be pulled from under us. Such a student no longer *needs* admiration to carry him over a series of obstacles (no matter how much he may need it for other reasons), and, in missing certain familiar objects of admiration, we are likely to conclude that such *conditions* are less admirable. Obstacles to scholarly work may serve as a useful measure of motivation—and we may go wrong unless some substitute is found but we can scarcely defend a deliberate harassment of the student for this purpose. The productivity of any set of conditions can be evaluated only when we have freed ourselves of the attitudes which have been generated in us as members of an ethical group.

A similar difficulty arises from our use of punishment in the form of censure or blame. The concept of responsibility and the related concepts of foreknowledge and choice are used to justify techniques of control using punishment. Was So-and-So aware of the probable consequences of his action, and was the action deliberate? If so, we are justified in punishing him. But what does this mean? It appears to be a question concerning the efficacy of the contingent relations between behavior and punishing consequences. We punish behavior because it is objectionable to us or the group, but in a minor refinement of rather recent origin we have come to withhold punishment when it cannot be expected to have any effect. If the objectionable consequences of an act were accidental and not likely to occur again, there is no point in punishing. We say that the individual was not "aware of the consequences of his action" or that the consequences were not "intentional." If the action could not have been avoided—if the individual "had no choice"—punishment is also withheld, as it is if the individual is incapable of being changed by punishment because he is of "unsound mind." In all these cases—different as they are—the individual is held "not responsible" and goes unpunished.

Just as we say that it is "not fair" to punish a man for something he could not help doing, so we call it "unfair" when one is rewarded beyond his due or for something he could not help doing. In other words, we also object to wasting *reinforcers* where they are not needed or will do no good. We make the same point with the words *just* and *right*. Thus we have no right to punish the irresponsible, and a man has no right to reinforcers he does not earn or deserve. But concepts of choice, responsibility, justice, and so on, provide a most inadequate analysis of efficient reinforcing and punishing contingencies because they carry a heavy semantic cargo of a quite different sort, which obscures any attempt to clarify controlling practices or to improve techniques. In particular, they fail to prepare us for techniques based on other than aversive techniques of control. Most people would object to forcing prisoners to serve as subjects of dangerous medical experiments, but few object when they are induced to serve by the offer of return privileges—even when the reinforcing effect of these privileges has been created by forcible deprivation. In the traditional scheme the right to refuse guarantees the individual against coercion or an unfair bargain. But to what extent *can* a prisoner refuse under such circumstances?

We need not go so far afield to make the point. We can observe our own attitude toward personal freedom in the way we resent any interference with what we want to do. Suppose we want to buy a car of a particular sort. Then we may object, for example, if our wife urges us to buy a less expensive model and to put the difference into a new refrigerator. Or we may resent it if our neighbor questions our need for such a car or our ability to pay for it. We would certainly resent it if it were illegal to buy such a car (remember Prohibition); and if we find we cannot actually afford it, we may resent governmental control of the price through tariffs and taxes. We resent it if we discover that we cannot get the car because the manufacturer is holding the model in deliberately short supply in order to push a model we do not want. In all this we assert our democratic right to buy the car of our choice. We are well prepared to do so and to resent any restriction on our freedom.

But why do we not ask *why* it is the car of our choice and resent the forces which made it so? Perhaps our favorite toy as a child was a car, of a very different model, but nevertheless bearing the name of the car we now want. Perhaps our favorite TV program is sponsored by the manufacturer of that car. Perhaps we have seen pictures of many beautiful or prestigeful persons driving it—in pleasant or glamorous places. Perhaps the car has been designed with respect to our motivational patterns: the device on the hood is a phallic symbol; or the horsepower has been stepped up to please our competitive spirit in enabling us to pass other cars swiftly (or, as the advertisements say, "safely"). The concept of freedom that has emerged as part of the cultural practice of our group makes little or no provision for recognizing or dealing with these kinds of control. Concepts like "responsibility" and "rights" are scarcely applicable. We are prepared to deal with coercive measures, but we have no traditional recourse with respect to other measures which in the long run (and especially with the help of science) may be much more powerful and dangerous.

Education

The techniques of education were once frankly aversive. The teacher was usually older and stronger than his pupils and was able to "make them learn." This meant that they were not actually taught but were surrounded by a threatening world from which they could escape only by learning. Usually they were left to their own resources in discovering how to do so. Claude Coleman has published a grimly amusing reminder of these older practices.[3] He tells of a schoolteacher who published a careful account of his services during 51 years of teaching, during which he administered: ". . . 911,527 blows with a cane; 124,010 with a rod; 20,989 with a ruler; 136,715 with the hand; 10,295 over the mouth; 7,905 boxes on the ear; [and] 1,115,800 slaps on the head. . . ."

Progressive education was a humanitarian effort to substitute positive reinforcement for such aversive measures, but in the search for useful human values in the classroom it has never fully replaced the variables it abandoned. Viewed as a branch of behavioral technology, education remains relatively inefficient. We supplement it, and rationalize it, by admiring the pupil who learns *for himself;* and we often attribute the learning process, or knowledge itself, to something *inside* the individual. We admire behavior which seems to have inner sources. Thus we admire one who *recites* a poem more than one who simply *reads* it. We admire one who *knows* the answer more than one who *knows where to look it up.* We admire the *writer* rather than the *reader.* We admire the arithmetician who can do a problem in his head rather than with a slide rule or calculating machine, or in "original" ways rather than by a strict application of rules. In general we feel that any aid or "crutch"—except those aids to which we are now thoroughly accustomed—reduces the credit due. In Plato's *Phaedus,* Thamus, the king, attacks the invention of the alphabet on similar

3. C. Coleman, *Bull. Am. Assoc. Univ. Professors* 39, 457 (1953).

grounds! He is afraid "it will produce forgetfulness in the minds of those who learn to use it, because they will not practice their memories. . . ." In other words, he holds it more admirable to remember than to use a memorandum. He also objects that pupils "will read many things without instruction . . . [and] will therefore seem to know many things when they are for the most part ignorant." In the same vein we are today sometimes contemptuous of book learning, but, as educators, we can scarcely afford to adopt this view without reservation.

By admiring the student for knowledge and blaming him for ignorance, we escape some of the responsibility of teaching him. We resist any analysis of the educational process which threatens the notion of inner wisdom or questions the contention that the fault of ignorance lies with the student. More powerful techniques which bring about the same changes in behavior by manipulating *external* variables are decried as brainwashing or thought control. We are quite unprepared to judge *effective* educational measures. As long as only a few pupils learn much of what is taught, we do not worry about uniformity or regimentation. We do not fear the feeble technique; but we should view with dismay a system under which every student learned everything listed in a syllabus—although such a condition is far from unthinkable. Similarly, we do not fear a system which is so defective that the student must *work* for an education; but we are loath to give credit for anything learned without effort—although this could well be taken as an ideal result—and we flatly refuse to give credit if the student already knows what a school teaches.

A world in which people are wise and good without trying, without "having to be," without "choosing to be," could conceivably be a far better world for everyone. In such a world we should not have to "give anyone credit"—we should not need to admire anyone—for being wise and good. From our present point of view we cannot believe that such a world would be admirable. We do not even permit ourselves to imagine what it would be like.

Government

Government has always been the special field of aversive control. The state is frequently defined in terms of the power to punish, and jurisprudence leans heavily upon the associated notion of personal responsibility. Yet it is becoming increasingly difficult to reconcile current practice and theory with these earlier views. In criminology, for example, there is a strong tendency to drop the notion of responsibility in favor of some such alternative as capacity or controllability. But no matter how strongly the facts, or even practical expedience, support such a change, it is difficult to make the change in a legal system designed on a different plan. When governments resort to other techniques (for example, positive reinforcement), the concept of responsibility is no longer relevant and the theory of government is no longer applicable.

The conflict is illustrated by two decisions of the Supreme Court in the 1930's which dealt with, and disagreed on, the definition of control or coercion.[4] The Agricultural Adjustment Act proposed that the Secretary of Agriculture make "rental or benefit payments" to those farmers who agreed to reduce production. The government agreed that the Act would be unconstitutional if the farmer had been *compelled* to reduce production but was not, since he was merely *invited* to do so. Justice Roberts[5] expressed the contrary majority view of the court that "The power to confer or withhold unlimited benefits is the power to coerce or destroy." This recognition of positive reinforcement was withdrawn a few years later in another case in which Justice Cardozo[6] wrote "To hold that motive or temptation is equivalent to coercion is to plunge the law in endless difficulties." We may agree with him, without implying that the proposition is therefore wrong. Sooner or later the law must be prepared to deal with all possible techniques of governmental control.

The uneasiness with which we view government (in the broadest possible sense) when it does not use punishment is shown by the reception of my utopian novel, *Walden Two*.[7] This was essentially a proposal to apply a behavioral technology to the construction of a workable, effective, and productive pattern of government. It was greeted with wrathful violence. *Life* magazine called it "a travesty on the good life," and "a menace . . . a triumph of mortmain or the dead hand not envisaged since the days of Sparta . . . a slur upon a name, a corruption of an impulse." Joseph Wood Krutch devoted a substantial part of his book, *The Measure of Man*,[8] to attacking my views and those of the protagonist, Frazier, in the same vein, and Morris Viteles has recently criticized the book in a similar manner in

4. P. A. Freund *et al., Constitutional Law: Cases and Other Problems,* vol. 1, p. 233 (Little, Brown, Boston, 1954).
5. *Ibid.*
6. *Ibid.,* p. 244.
7. B. F. Skinner, *Walden Two* (Macmillan, New York, 1948).
8. J. W. Krutch, *The Measure of Man* (Bobbs-Merrill, Indianapolis, 1953).

Science.[9]—Perhaps the reaction is best expressed in a quotation from *The Quest for Utopia* by Negley and Patrick[10]:

"Halfway through this contemporary utopia, the reader may feel sure, as we did, that this is a beautifully ironic satire on what has been called 'behavioral engineering.' The longer one stays in this better world of the psychologist, however, the plainer it becomes that the inspiration is not satiric, but messianic. This is indeed the behaviorally engineered society, and while it was to be expected that sooner or later the principle of psychological conditioning would be made the basis of a serious construction of utopia—Brown anticipated it in *Limanora*—yet not even the effective satire of Huxley is adequate preparation for the shocking horror of the idea when positively presented. Of all the dictatorships espoused by utopists, this is the most profound, and incipient dictators might well find in this utopia a guidebook of political practice."

One would scarcely guess that the authors are talking about a world in which there is food, clothing, and shelter for all, where everyone chooses his own work and works on the average only 4 hours a day, where music and the arts flourish, where personal relationships develop under the most favorable circumstances, where education prepares every child for the social and intellectual life which lies before him, where—in short—people are truly happy, secure, productive, creative, and forward-looking. What is wrong with it? Only one thing: someone "planned it that way." If these critics had come upon a society in some remote corner of the world which boasted similar advantages, they would undoubtedly have hailed it as providing a pattern we all might well follow—provided that it was clearly the result of a natural process of cultural evolution. Any evidence that intelligence had been used in arriving at this version of the good life would, in their eyes, be a serious flaw. No matter if the planner of *Walden Two* diverts none of the proceeds of the community to his own use, no matter if he has no current control or is, indeed, unknown to most of the other members of the community (he planned that, too), somewhere back of it all he occupies the position of prime mover. And this, to the child of the democratic tradition, spoils it all.

The dangers inherent in the control of human behavior are very real. The possibility of the misuse of scientific knowledge must always be faced. We cannot escape by denying the power of a science of behavior or arresting its development. It is no help to cling to familiar

9. M. Viteles, *Science* 122, 1167 (1955).

10. G. Negley and J. M. Patrick, *The Quest for Utopia* (Schuman, New York, 1952).

philosophies of human behavior simply because they are more reassuring. As I have pointed out elsewhere,[11] the new techniques emerging from a science of behavior must be subject to the explicit counter-control which has already been applied to earlier and cruder forms. Brute force and deception, for example, are now fairly generally suppressed by ethical practices and by explicit governmental and religious agencies. A similar countercontrol of scientific knowledge in the interests of the group is a feasible and promising possibility. Although we cannot say how devious the course of its evolution may be, a cultural pattern of control and countercontrol will presumably emerge which will be most widely supported because it is most widely reinforcing.

If we cannot foresee all the details of this (as we obviously cannot), it is important to remember that this is true of the critics of science as well. The dire consequences of new techniques of control, the hidden menace in original cultural designs—these need some proof. It is only another example of my present point that the need for proof is so often overlooked. Man has got himself into some pretty fixes, and it is easy to believe that he will do so again. But there is a more optimistic possibility. The slow growth of the methods of science, now for the first time being applied to human affairs, *may* mean a new and exciting phase of human life to which historical analogies will not apply and in which earlier political slogans will not be appropriate. If we are to use the knowledge that a science of behavior is now making available with any hope of success, we must look at human nature as it is brought into focus through the methods of science rather than as it has been presented to us in a series of historical accidents.

If the advent of a powerful science of behavior causes trouble, it will not be because science itself is inimical to human welfare but because older conceptions have not yielded easily or gracefully. We expect resistance to new techniques of control from those who have heavy investments in the old, but we have no reason to help them preserve a series of principles that are not ends in themselves but rather outmoded means to an end. What is needed is a new conception of human behavior which is compatible with the implications of a scientific analysis. All men control and are controlled. The question of government in the broadest possible sense is not how freedom is to be preserved but what kinds of control are to be used and to what ends. Control must be analyzed and considered in its proper proportions. No one, I am sure, wishes to develop new master-slave relationships

11. B. F. Skinner, *Trans. N.Y. Acad. Sci.* 17, 547 (1955).

or bend the will of the people to despotic rulers in new ways. These are patterns of control appropriate to a world without science. They may well be the first to go when the experimental analysis of behavior comes into its own in the design of cultural practices.

ROGERS

There are, I believe, a number of matters in connection with this important topic on which the authors of this article, and probably a large majority of psychologists, are in agreement. These matters then are not issues as far as we are concerned, and I should like to mention them briefly in order to put them to one side.

Points of Agreement

I am sure we agree that men—as individuals and as societies—have always endeavored to understand, predict, influence, and control human behavior—their own behavior and that of others.

I believe we agree that the behavioral sciences are making and will continue to make increasingly rapid progress in the understanding of behavior, and that as a consequence the capacity to predict and to control behavior is developing with equal rapidity.

I believe we agree that to deny these advances, or to claim that man's behavior cannot be a field of science, is unrealistic. Even though this is not an issue for us, we should recognize that many intelligent men still hold strongly to the view that the actions of men are free in some sense such that scientific knowledge of man's behavior is impossible. Thus Reinhold Niebuhr, the noted theologian, heaps scorn on the concept of psychology as a science of man's behavior and even says, "In any event, no scientific investigation of past behavior can become the basis of predictions of future behavior." [12] So, while this is not an issue for psychologists, we should at least notice in passing that it is an issue for many people.

I believe we are in agreement that the tremendous potential power of a science which permits the prediction and control of behavior may be misused, and that the possibility of such misuse constitutes a serious threat.

12. R. Niebuhr, *The Self and the Dramas of History* (Scribner, New York, 1955), p. 47.

Consequently Skinner and I are in agreement that the whole question of the scientific control of human behavior is a matter with which psychologists and the general public should concern themselves. As Robert Oppenheimer told the American Psychological Association last year[13] the problems that psychologists will pose for society by their growing ability to control behavior will be much more grave than the problems posed by the ability of physicists to control the reactions of matter. I am not sure whether psychologists generally recognize this. My impression is that by and large they hold a laissez-faire attitude. Obviously Skinner and I do not hold this laissez-faire view, or we would not have written this article.

Points at Issue

With these several points of basic and important agreement, are there then any issues that remain on which there are differences? I believe there are. They can be stated very briefly: Who will be controlled? Who will exercise control? What type of control will be exercised? Most important of all, toward what end or what purpose, or in the pursuit of what value, will control be exercised?

It is on questions of this sort that there exist ambiguities, misunderstandings, and probably deep differences. These differences exist among psychologists, among members of the general public in this country, and among various world cultures. Without any hope of achieving a final resolution of these questions, we can, I believe, put these issues in clearer form.

Some Meanings

To avoid ambiguity and faulty communication, I would like to clarify the meanings of some of the terms we are using.

Behavioral science is a term that might be defined from several angles but in the context of this discussion it refers primarily to knowledge that the existence of certain describable conditions in the human being and/or in his environment is followed by certain describable consequences in his actions.

Prediction means the prior identification of behaviors which then occur. Because it is important in some things I wish to say later, I

---

13. R. Oppenheimer, *Am. Psychol.* 11, 127 (1956).

would point out that one may predict a highly specific behavior, such as an eye blink, or one may predict a class of behaviors. One might correctly predict "avoidant behavior," for example, without being able to specify whether the individual will run away or simply close his eyes.

The word *control* is a very slippery one, which can be used with any one of several meanings. I would like to specify three that seem most important for our present purposes. *Control* may mean: (i) The setting of conditions by B for A, A having no voice in the matter, such that certain predictable behaviors then occur in A. I refer to this as external control. (ii) The setting of conditions by B for A, A giving some degree of consent to these conditions, such that certain predictable behaviors then occur in A. I refer to this as the influence of B on A. (iii) The setting of conditions by A such that certain predictable behaviors then occur in himself. I refer to this as internal control. It will be noted that Skinner lumps together the first two meanings, external control and influence, under the concept of control. I find this confusing.

Usual Concept of Control of Human Behavior

With the underbrush thus cleared away (I hope), let us review very briefly the various elements that are involved in the usual concept of the control of human behavior as mediated by the behavorial sciences. I am drawing here on the previous writings of Skinner, on his present statements, on the writings of others who have considered in either friendly or antagonistic fashion the meanings that would be involved in such control. I have not excluded the science fiction writers, as reported recently by Vandenberg,[14] since they often show an awareness of the issues involved, even though the methods described are as yet fictional. These then are the elements that seem common to these different concepts of the application of science to human behavior.

1) There must first be some sort of decision about goals. Usually desirable goals are assumed, but sometimes, as in George Orwell's book *1984*, the goal that is selected is an aggrandizement of individual power with which most of us would disagree. In a recent paper Skinner suggests that one possible set of goals to be assigned to the behavioral technology is this: "Let men be happy, informed, skillful, well-behaved and productive." [15] In the first draft of his part of this article,

14. S. G. Vandenberg, *ibid.* 11, 339 (1956).
15. B. F. Skinner, *Am. Scholar* 25, 47 (1955–56).

which he was kind enough to show me, he did not mention such definite goals as these, but desired "improved" educational practices, "wiser" use of knowledge in government, and the like. In the final version of his article he avoids even these value-laden terms, and his implicit goal is the very general one that scientific control of behavior is desirable, because it would perhaps bring "a far better world for everyone."

Thus the first step in thinking about the control of human behavior is the choice of goals, whether specific or general. It is necessary to come to terms in some way with the issue, "For what purpose?"

2) A second element is that, whether the end selected is highly specific or is a very general one such as wanting "a better world," we proceed by the methods of science to discover the means to these ends. We continue through further experimentation and investigation to discover more effective means. The method of science is self-correcting in thus arriving at increasingly effective ways of achieving the purpose we have in mind.

3) The third aspect of such control is that as the conditions or methods are discovered by which to reach the goal, some person or some group establishes these conditions and uses these methods, having in one way or another obtained the power to do so.

4) The fourth element is the exposure of individuals to the prescribed conditions, and this leads, with a high degree of probability, to behavior which is in line with the goals desired. Individuals are now happy, if that has been the goal, or well-behaved, or submissive, or whatever it has been decided to make them.

5) The fifth element is that if the process I have described is put in motion then there is a continuing social organization which will continue to produce the types of behavior that have been valued.

Some Flaws

Are there any flaws in this way of viewing the control of human behavior? I believe there are. In fact the only element in this description with which I find myself in agreement is the second. It seems to me quite incontrovertibly true that the scientific method is an excellent way to discover the means by which to achieve our goals. Beyond that, I feel many sharp differences, which I will try to spell out.

I believe that in Skinner's presentation here and in his previous writings, there is a serious underestimation of the problem of power. To hope that the power which is being made available by the behavioral sciences will be exercised by the scientist, or by a benevolent group, seems to me a hope little supported by either recent or distant history. It seems far more likely that behavioral scientists, holding their present attitudes, will be in the position of the German rocket scientists specializing in guided missiles. First they worked devotedly for Hitler to destroy the U.S.S.R. and the United States. Now, depending on who captured them, they work devotedly for the U.S.S.R. in the interest of destroying the United States, or devotedly for the United States in the interest of destroying the U.S.S.R. If behavioral scientists are concerned solely with advancing their science, it seems most probable that they will serve the purposes of whatever individual or group has the power.

But the major flaw I see in this review of what is involved in the scientific control of human behavior is the denial, misunderstanding, or gross underestimation of the place of ends, goals or values in their relationship to science. This error (as it seems to me) has so many implications that I would like to devote some space to it.

Ends and Values in Relation to Science

In sharp contradiction to some views that have been advanced, I would like to propose a two-pronged thesis: (i) In any scientific endeavor—whether "pure" or applied science—there is a prior subjective choice of the purpose or value which that scientific work is perceived as serving. (ii) This subjective value choice which brings the scientific endeavor into being must always lie outside of that endeavor and can never become a part of the science involved in that endeavor.

Let me illustrate the first point from Skinner himself. It is clear that in his earlier writing it is recognized that a prior value choice is necessary, and it is specified as the goal that men are to become happy, well-behaved, productive, and so on. I am pleased that Skinner has retreated from the goals he then chose, because to me they seem to be stultifying values. I can only feel that he was choosing these goals for others, not for himself. I would hate to see Skinner become "well-behaved," as that term would be defined for him by behavioral scientists. His recent article in the *American Psychologist*[16] shows that he certainly does not want to be "productive" as that value is defined by most psychologists. And the most awful fate I can imagine for him

16. ———, *Am. Psychol.* 11, 221 (1956).

would be to have him constantly "happy." It is the fact that he is very unhappy about many things which makes me prize him.

In the first draft of his part of this article, he also included such prior value choices, saying for example, "We must decide how we are to use the knowledge which a science of human behavior is now making available." Now he has dropped all mention of such choices, and if I understand him correctly, he believes that science can proceed without them. He has suggested this view in another recent paper, stating that "We must continue to experiment in cultural design . . . testing the consequences as we go. Eventually the practices which make for the greatest biological and psychological strength of the group will presumably survive." [17]

I would point out, however, that to choose to experiment is a value choice. Even to move in the direction of perfectly random experimentation is a value choice. To test the consequences of an experiment is possible only if we have first made a subjective choice of a criterion value. And implicit in his statement is a valuing of biological and psychological strength. So even when trying to avoid such choice, it seems inescapable that a prior subjective value choice is necessary for any scientific endeavor, or for any application of scientific knowledge.

I wish to make it clear that I am not saying that values cannot be included as a subject of science. It is not true that science deals only with certain classes of "facts" and that these classes do not include values. It is a bit more complex than that, as a simple illustration or two may make clear.

If I value knowledge of the "three R's" as a goal of education, the methods of science can give me increasingly accurate information on how this goal may be achieved. If I value problem-solving ability as a goal of education, the scientific method can give me the same kind of help.

Now, if I wish to determine whether problem-solving ability is "better" than knowledge of the three R's, then scientific method can also study those two values but *only*—and this is very important—in terms of some other value which I have subjectively chosen. I may value college success. Then I can determine whether problem-solving ability or knowledge of the three R's is most closely associated with that value. I may value personal integration or vocational success or responsible citizenship. I can determine whether problem-solving ability or knowledge of the three R's is "better" for achieving any one of these values. But the value or purpose that gives meaning to a particular scientific endeavor must always lie outside of that endeavor.

Although our concern in this symposium is largely with applied science, what I have been saying seems equally true of so-called "pure" science. In pure science the usual prior subjective value choice is the discovery of truth. But this is a subjective choice, and science can never say whether it is the best choice, save in the light of some other value. Geneticists in the U.S.S.R., for example, had to make a subjective choice of whether it was better to pursue truth or to discover facts which upheld a governmental dogma. Which choice is "better"? We could make a scientific investigation of those alternatives but only in the light of some other subjectively chosen value. If, for example, we value the survival of a culture, then we could begin to investigate with the methods of science the question of whether pursuit of truth or support of governmental dogma is most closely associated with cultural survival.

My point then is that any endeavor in science, pure or applied, is carried on in the pursuit of a purpose or value that is subjectively chosen by persons. It is important that this choice be made explicit, since the particular value which is being sought can never be tested or evaluated, confirmed or denied, by the scientific endeavor to which it gives birth. The initial purpose or value always and necessarily lies outside the scope of the scientific effort which it sets in motion.

Among other things this means that if we choose some particular goal or series of goals for human beings and then set out on a large scale to control human behavior to the end of achieving those goals, we are locked in the rigidity of our initial choice, because such a scientific endeavor can never transcend itself to select new goals. Only subjective human persons can do that. Thus if we chose as our goal the state of happiness for human beings (a goal deservedly ridiculed by Aldous Huxley in *Brave New World*), and if we involved all of society in a successful scientific program by which people became happy, we would be locked in a colossal rigidity in which no one would be free to question this goal, because our scientific operations could not transcend themselves to question their guiding purposes. And without laboring this point, I would remark that colossal rigidity, whether in dinosaurs or dictatorships, has a very poor record of evolutionary survival.

If, however, a part of our scheme is to set free some "planners" who do not have to be happy, who are not controlled, and who are therefore free to choose other values, this has several meanings. It means that the purpose we have chosen as our goal is not a sufficient and a satisfying one for human beings but must be supplemented. It also means that if it is necessary to set up an elite group which is free, then this shows all too clearly that the great majority are only the slaves—no matter by what high-sounding name we call them—of those who select the goals.

Perhaps, however, the thought is that a continuing scientific endeavor will evolve its own goals; that the initial findings will alter the directions, and subsequent findings will alter them still further, and that science somehow develops its own purpose. Although he does not clearly say so, this appears to be the pattern Skinner has in mind. It is surely a reasonable description, but it overlooks one element in this continuing development, which is that subjective personal choice enters in at every point at which the direction changes. The findings of a science, the results of an experiment, do not and never can tell us what next scientific purpose to pursue. Even in the purest of science, the scientist must decide what the findings mean and must subjectively choose what next step will be most profitable in the pursuit of his purpose. And if we are speaking of the application of scientific knowledge, then it is distressingly clear that the increasing scientific knowledge of the structure of the atom carries with it no necessary choice as to the purpose to which this knowledge will be put. This is a subjective personal choice which must be made by many individuals.

Thus I return to the proposition with which I began this section of my remarks—and which I now repeat in different words. Science has its meaning as the objective pursuit of a purpose which has been subjectively chosen by a person or persons. This purpose or value can never be investigated by the particular scientific experiment or investigation to which it has given birth and meaning. Consequently, any discussion of the control of human beings by the behavioral sciences must first and most deeply concern itself with the subjectively chosen purposes which such an application of science is intended to implement.

Is the Situation Hopeless?

The thoughtful reader may recognize that, although my remarks up to this point have introduced some modifications in the conception of the processes by which human behavior will be controlled, these remarks may have made such control seem, if anything, even more inevitable. We might sum it up this way: Behavioral science is clearly moving forward; the increasing power for control which it gives will be held by someone or some group; such an individual or group will surely choose the values or goals to be achieved; and most of us will then be increasingly controlled by means so subtle that we will not even be aware of them as controls. Thus, whether a council of wise psychologists (if this is not a contradiction in terms), or a Stalin, or a Big Brother has the power, and whether the goal is happiness, or productivity, or resolution of the Oedipus complex, or submission, or love of Big Brother, we will inevitably find ourselves moving toward the chosen goal and probably thinking that we ourselves desire it. Thus, if this line of reasoning is correct, it appears that some form of *Walden Two* or of *1984* (and at a deep philosophic level they seem indistinguishable) is coming. The fact that it would surely arrive piecemeal, rather than all at once, does not greatly change the fundamental issues. In any event, as Skinner has indicated in his writings, we would then look back upon the concepts of human freedom, the capacity for choice, the responsibility for choice, and the worth of the human individual as historical curiosities which once existed by cultural accident as values in a prescientific civilization.

I believe that any person observant of trends must regard something like the foregoing sequence as a real possibility. It is not simply a fantasy. Something of that sort may even be the most likely future. But is it an inevitable future? I want to devote the remainder of my remarks to an alternative possibility.

Alternative Set of Values

Suppose we start with a set of ends, values, purposes, quite different from the type of goals we have been considering. Suppose we do this quite openly, setting them forth as a possible value choice to be accepted or rejected. Suppose we select a set of values that focuses on fluid elements of process rather than static attributes. We might then value: man as a process of becoming, as a process of achieving worth and dignity through the development of his potentialities; the individual human being as a self-actualizing process, moving on to more challenging and enriching experiences; the process by which the individual creatively adapts to an ever-new and changing world; the process by which knowledge transcends itself, as, for example, the theory of relativity transcended Newtonian physics, itself to be transcended in some future day by a new perception.

If we select values such as these we turn to our science and technology of behavior with a very different set of questions. We will want to know such things as these: Can science aid in the discovery of new modes of richly rewarding living? more meaningful and satisfying modes of interpersonal relationships? Can science inform us on how the human race can become a more intelligent participant in its own evolution—its physical, psychological and social evolution? Can science inform us on ways of releasing the creative capacity of individuals, which seem so necessary if we are to survive in this fantastically expanding atomic age? Oppenheimer has pointed out[18] that knowledge, which used to double in millennia or centuries, now doubles in a generation or a decade. It appears that we must discover the utmost in release of creativity if we are to be able to adapt effectively. In short, can science discover the methods by which man can most readily become a continually developing and self-transcending process, in his behavior, his thinking, his knowledge? Can science predict and release an essentially "unpredictable" freedom?

It is one of the virtues of science as a method that it is as able to advance and implement goals and purposes of this sort as it is to serve static values, such as states of being well-informed, happy, obedient. Indeed we have some evidence of this.

Small Example

I will perhaps be forgiven if I document some of the possibilities along this line by turning to psychotherapy, the field I know best.

Psychotherapy, as Meerloo[19] and others have pointed out, can be one of the most subtle tools for the control of *A* by *B*. The therapist can subtly mold individuals in imitation of himself. He can cause an individual to become a submissive and conforming being. When certain therapeutic principles are used in extreme fashion, we call it brainwashing, an instance of the disintegration of the personality and a reformulation of the person along lines desired by the controlling individual. So the principles of therapy can be used as an effective means of external control of human personality and behavior. Can psychotherapy be anything else?

Here I find the developments going on in client-centered psychotherapy[20] an exciting hint of what a behavioral science can do in achieving the kinds of values I have stated. Quite aside from being a somewhat new orientation in psychotherapy, this development has

18. R. Oppenheimer, *Roosevelt University Occasional Papers* 2 (1956).
19. J. A. M. Meerloo, *J. Nervous Mental Disease* 122, 353 (1955).
20. C. R. Rogers, *Client-Centered Therapy* (Houghton-Mifflin, Boston, 1951).

important implications regarding the relation of a behavioral science to the control of human behavior. Let me describe our experience as it relates to the issues of this discussion.

In client-centered therapy, we are deeply engaged in the prediction and influencing of behavior, or even the control of behavior. As therapists, we institute certain attitudinal conditions, and the client has relatively little voice in the establishment of these conditions. We predict that if these conditions are instituted, certain behavioral consequences will ensue in the client. Up to this point this is largely external control, no different from what Skinner has described, and no different from what I have discussed in the preceding sections of this article. But here any similarity ceases.

The conditions we have chosen to establish predict such behavioral consequences as these: that the client will become self-directing, less rigid, more open to the evidence of his senses, better organized and integrated, more similar to the ideal which he has chosen for himself. In other words, we have established by external control conditions which we predict will be followed by internal control by the individual, in pursuit of internally chosen goals. We have set the conditions which predict various classes of behaviors—self-directing behaviors, sensitivity to realities within and without, flexible adaptiveness—which are by their very nature unpredictable in their specifics. Our recent research[21] indicates that our predictions are to a significant degree corroborated, and our commitment to the scientific method causes us to believe that more effective means of achieving these goals may be realized.

Research exists in other fields—industry, education, group dynamics —which seems to support our own findings. I believe it may be conservatively stated that scientific progress has been made in identifying those conditions in an interpersonal relationship which, if they exist in *B*, are followed in *A* by greater maturity in behavior, less dependence on others, an increase in expressiveness as a person, an increase in variability, flexibility and effectiveness of adaptation, an increase in self-responsibility and self-direction. And, quite in contrast to the concern expressed by some, we do not find that the creatively adaptive behavior which results from such self-directed variability of expression is a "happy accident" which occurs in "chaos." Rather, the individual who is open to his experience, and self-directing, is harmonious not chaotic, ingenious rather than random, as he orders his responses im-

21. —— and R. Dymond, Eds., *Psychotherapy and Personality Change* (Univ. of Chicago Press, Chicago, 1954).

aginatively toward the achievement of his own purposes. His creative actions are no more a "happy accident" than was Einstein's development of the theory of relativity.

Thus we find ourselves in fundamental agreement with John Dewey's statement: "Science has made its way by releasing, not by suppressing, the elements of variation, of invention and innovation, of novel creation in individuals." [22] Progress in personal life and in group living is, we believe, made in the same way.

Possible Concept of the Control of Human Behavior

It is quite clear that the point of view I am expressing is in sharp contrast to the usual conception of the relationship of the behavioral sciences to the control of human behavior. In order to make this contrast even more blunt, I will state this possibility in paragraphs parallel to those used before.

1) It is possible for us to choose to value man as a self-actualizing process of becoming; to value creativity, and the process by which knowledge becomes self-transcending.

2) We can proceed, by the methods of science, to discover the conditions which necessarily precede these processes and, through continuing experimentation, to discover better means of achieving these purposes.

3) It is possible for individuals or groups to set these conditions, with a minimum of power or control. According to present knowledge, the only authority necessary is the authority to establish certain qualities of interpersonal relationship.

4) Exposed to these conditions, present knowledge suggests that individuals become more self-responsible, make progress in self-actualization, become more flexible, and become more creatively adaptive.

5) Thus such an initial choice would inaugurate the beginnings of a social system or subsystem in which values, knowledge, adaptive skills, and even the concept of science would be continually changing and self-transcending. The emphasis would be upon man as a process of becoming.

I believe it is clear that such a view as I have been describing does not lead to any definable utopia. It would be impossible to predict its final outcome. It involves a step-by-step development, based on a

22. J. Ratner, Ed., *Intelligence in the Modern World: John Dewey's Philosophy* (Modern Library, New York, 1939), p. 359.

continuing subjective choice of purposes, which are implemented by the behavioral sciences. It is in the direction of the "open society," as that term has been defined by Popper,[23] where individuals carry responsibility for personal decisions. It is at the opposite pole from his concept of the closed society, of which *Walden Two* would be an example.

I trust it is also evident that the whole emphasis is on process, not on end-states of being. I am suggesting that it is by choosing to value certain qualitative elements of the process of becoming that we can find a pathway toward the open society.

The Choice

It is my hope that we have helped to clarify the range of choice which will lie before us and our children in regard to the behavioral sciences. We can choose to use our growing knowledge to enslave people in ways never dreamed of before, depersonalizing them, controlling them by means so carefully selected that they will perhaps never be aware of their loss of personhood. We can choose to utilize our scientific knowledge to make men happy, well-behaved, and productive, as Skinner earlier suggested. Or we can insure that each person learns all the syllabus which we select and set before him, as Skinner now suggests. Or at the other end of the spectrum of choice we can choose to use the behavioral sciences in ways which will free, not control; which will bring about constructive variability, not conformity; which will develop creativity, not contentment; which will facilitate each person in his self-directed process of becoming; which will aid individuals, groups, and even the concept of science to become self-transcending in freshly adaptive ways of meeting life and its problems. The choice is up to us, and, the human race being what it is, we are likely to stumble about, making at times some nearly disastrous value choices and at other times highly constructive ones.

I am aware that to some, this setting forth of a choice is unrealistic, because a choice of values is regarded as not possible. Skinner has stated: "Man's vaunted creative powers . . . his capacity to choose and our right to hold him responsible for his choice—none of these is conspicuous in this new self-portrait (provided by science). Man, we once believed, was free to express himself in art, music, and liter-

23. K. R. Popper, *The Open Society and Its Enemies* (Rutledge and Kegan Paul, London, 1945).

ature, to inquire into nature, to seek salvation in his own way. He could initiate action and make spontaneous and capricious changes of course. . . . But science insists that action is initiated by forces impinging upon the individual, and that caprice is only another name for behavior for which we have not yet found a cause." [24]

I can understand this point of view, but I believe that it avoids looking at the great paradox of behavioral science. Behavior, when it is examined scientifically, is surely best understood as determined by prior causation. This is one great fact of science. But responsible personal choice, which is the most essential element in being a person, which is the core experience in psychotherapy, which exists prior to any scientific endeavor, is an equally prominent fact in our lives. To deny the experience of responsible choice is, to me, as restricted a view as to deny the possibility of a behavioral science. That these two important elements of our experience appear to be in contradiction has perhaps the same significance as the contradiction between the wave theory and the corpuscular theory of light, both of which can be shown to be true, even though incompatible. We cannot profitably deny our subjective life, any more than we can deny the objective description of that life.

In conclusion then, it is my contention that science cannot come into being without a personal choice of the values we wish to achieve. And these values we choose to implement will forever lie outside of the science which implements them; the goals we select, the purposes we wish to follow, must always be outside of the science which achieves them. To me this has the encouraging meaning that the human person, with his capacity of subjective choice, can and will always exist, separate from and prior to any of his scientific undertakings. Unless as individuals and groups we choose to relinquish our capacity of subjective choice, we will always remain persons, not simply pawns of a self-created science.

SKINNER

I cannot quite agree that the practice of science *requires* a prior decision about goals or a prior choice of values. The metallurgist can study the properties of steel and the engineer can design a bridge without raising the question of whether a bridge is to be built. But

24. B. F. Skinner, *Am. Scholar* 25, 52–53 (1955–56).

such questions are certainly frequently raised and tentatively answered. Rogers wants to call the answers "subjective choices of values." To me, such an expression suggests that we have had to abandon more rigorous scientific practices in order to talk about our own behavior. In the experimental analysis of other organisms I would use other terms, and I shall try to do so here. Any list of values is a list of reinforcers —conditioned or otherwise. We are so constituted that under certain circumstances food, water, sexual contact, and so on, will make any behavior which produces them more likely to occur again. Other things may acquire this power. We do not need to say that an organism chooses to eat rather than to starve. If you answer that it is a very different thing when a man chooses to starve, I am only too happy to agree. If it were not so, we should have cleared up the question of choice long ago. An organism can be reinforced by—can be made to "choose"—almost any given state of affairs.

Rogers is concerned with choices that involve multiple and usually conflicting consequences. I have dealt with some of these elsewhere[25] in an analysis of self-control. Shall I eat these delicious strawberries today if I will then suffer an annoying rash tomorrow? The decision I am to make used to be assigned to the province of ethics. But we are now studying similar combinations of positive and negative consequences, as well as collateral conditions which affect the result, in the laboratory. Even a pigeon can be taught some measure of self-control! And this work helps us to understand the operation of certain formulas—among them value judgments—which folk-wisdom, religion, and psychotherapy have advanced in the interests of self-discipline. The observable effect of any statement of value is to alter the relative effectiveness of reinforcers. We may no longer enjoy the strawberries for thinking about the rash. If rashes are made sufficiently shameful, illegal, sinful, maladjusted, or unwise, we may glow with satisfaction as we push the strawberries aside in a grandiose avoidance response which would bring a smile to the lips of Murray Sidman.

People behave in ways which, as we say, conform to ethical, governmental, or religious patterns because they are reinforced for doing so. The resulting behavior may have far-reaching consequences for the survival of the pattern to which it conforms. And whether we like it or not, survival is the ultimate criterion. This is where, it seems to me, science can help—not in choosing a goal, but in enabling us to predict the survival value of cultural practices. Man has too long tried to get the kind of world he wants by glorifying some brand of

25. B. F. Skinner, *Science and Human Behavior* (Macmillan, New York, 1953).

immediate reinforcement. As science points up more and more of the remoter consequences, he may begin to work to strengthen behavior, not in a slavish devotion to a chosen value, but with respect to the ultimate survival of mankind. Do not ask me why I want mankind to survive. I can tell you why only in the sense in which the physiologist can tell you why I want to breathe. Once the relation between a given step and the survival of my group has been pointed out, I will take that step. And it is the business of science to point out just such relations.

The values I have occasionally recommended (and Rogers has not led me to recant) are transitional. Other things being equal, I am betting on the group whose practices make for healthy, happy, secure, productive, and creative people. And I insist that the values recommended by Rogers are transitional, too, for I can ask him the same kind of question. Man as a process of becoming—*what?* Self-actualization—for what? Inner control is no more a goal than external.

What Rogers seems to me to be proposing, both here and elsewhere,[26] is this: Let us use our increasing power of control to create individuals who will not need and perhaps will no longer respond to control. Let us solve the problem of our power by renouncing it. At first blush this seems as implausible as a benevolent despot. Yet power has occasionally been foresworn. A nation has burned its Reichstag, rich men have given away their wealth, beautiful women have become ugly hermits in the desert, and psychotherapists have become nondirective. When this happens, I look to other possible reinforcements for a plausible explanation. A people relinquish democratic power when a tyrant promises them the earth. Rich men give away wealth to escape the accusing finger of their fellowmen. A woman destroys her beauty in the hope of salvation. And a psychotherapist relinquishes control because he can thus help his client more effectively.

The solution that Rogers is suggesting is thus understandable. But is he correctly interpreting the result? What evidence is there that a client ever becomes truly *self*-directing? What evidence is there that he ever makes a truly *inner* choice of ideal or goal? Even though the therapist does not do the choosing, even though he encourages "self-actualization"—he is not out of control as long as he holds himself ready to step in when occasion demands—when, for example, the client chooses the goal of becoming a more accomplished liar or murdering his boss. But supposing the therapist does withdraw completely or is no longer necessary—what about all the other forces acting upon

26. C. R. Rogers, *Teachers College Record* 57, 316 (1956).

the client? Is the self-chosen goal independent of his early ethical and religious training? of the folk-wisdom of his group? of the opinions and attitudes of others who are important to him? Surely not. The therapeutic situation is only a small part of the world of the client. From the therapist's point of view it may appear to be possible to relinquish control. But the control passes, not to a "self," but to forces in other parts of the client's world. The solution of the therapist's problem of power cannot be *our* solution, for we must consider *all* the forces acting upon the individual.

The child who must be prodded and nagged is something less than a fully developed human being. We want to see him hurrying to his appointment, not because each step is taken in response to verbal reminders from his mother, but because certain temporal contingencies, in which dawdling has been punished and hurrying reinforced, have worked a change in his behavior. Call this a state of better organization, a greater sensitivity to reality, or what you will. The plain fact is that the child passes from a temporary verbal control exercised by his parents to control by certain inexorable features of the environment. I should suppose that something of the same sort happens in successful psychotherapy. Rogers seems to me to be saying this: Let us put an end, as quickly as possible, to any pattern of master-and-slave, to any direct obedience to command, to the submissive following of suggestions. Let the individual be free to adjust himself to more rewarding features of the world about him. In the end, let his teachers and counselors "wither away," like the Marxist state. I not only agree with this as a useful ideal, I have constructed a fanciful world to demonstrate its advantages. It saddens me to hear Rogers say that "at a deep philosophic level" *Walden Two* and George Orwell's *1984* "seem indistinguishable." They could scarcely be more unlike—at any level. The book *1984* is a picture of immediate aversive control for vicious selfish purposes. The founder of *Walden Two*, on the other hand, has built a community in which neither he nor any other person exerts any *current* control. His achievement lay in his original *plan*, and when he boasts of this ("It is enough to satisfy the thirstiest tyrant") we do not fear him but only pity him for his weakness.

Another critic of *Walden Two*, Andrew Hacker[27] has discussed this point in considering the bearing of mass conditioning upon the liberal notion of autonomous man. In drawing certain parallels between the Grand Inquisition passage in Dostoevsky's *Brothers Karamazov*, Hux-

27. A. Hacker, *J. Politics* 17, 590 1955).

ley's *Brave New World,* and *Walden Two,* he attempts to set up a distinction to be drawn in any society between conditioners and conditioned. He assumes that "the conditioner can be said to be autonomous in the traditional liberal sense." But then he notes: "Of course the conditioner has been conditioned. But he has not been conditioned by the conscious manipulation of another *person.*" But how does this affect the resulting behavior? Can we not soon forget the origins of the "artificial" diamond which is identical with the real thing? Whether it is an "accidental" cultural pattern, such as is said to have produced the founder of *Walden Two,* or the engineered environment which is about to produce his successors, we are dealing with sets of conditions generating human behavior which will ultimately be measured by their contribution to the strength of the group. We look to the future, not the past, for the test of "goodness" or acceptability.

If we are worthy of our democratic heritage we shall, of course, be ready to resist any tyrannical use of science for immediate or selfish purposes. But if we value the achievements and goals of democracy we must not refuse to apply science to the design and construction of cultural patterns, even though we may then find ourselves in some sense in the position of controllers. Fear of control, generalized beyond any warrant, has led to a misinterpretation of valid practices and the blind rejection of intelligent planning for a better way of life. in terms which I trust Rogers will approve, in conquering this fear we shall become more mature and better organized and shall, thus, more fully actualize ourselves as human beings.

5 / THE IMPACT OF TECHNOLOGY ON POLITICAL VALUES

Having examined the threats of technology to basic values in the previous parts, we turn in this part to the threats of the technological society to our democratic forms of government and to considerations of how we can overcome those threats.

Because American society always suffers from great political conflicts and experiences almost continual change of various kinds, and because these conflicts and changes are the result of many complex factors, it is very difficult to determine whether any given conflicts and changes are the result of short-term factors or of longer-run factors such as science and technology. For example, it is clear that many of the problems experienced by the United States in recent years, such as those stemming from the war in Indochina, are due partly to many specific, local, and short-run factors, such as miscalculations by executive officers in the government. But at the same time, some of our problems in recent years, such as the great increase in unemployed and poor blacks in the northern and western cities, have been reasonably direct results of technological changes, such as technological developments on southern farms, which drive out the marginal farmers.

In spite of the difficulty of separating out the short-run factors from the long-run factors of science and technology, we have every reason to believe that the social changes being produced by science and technology are having an increasing impact on our political institutions and political values. Each of the essays in this section attempts to get at the fundamental nature of this impact to analyze its consequences and to try to provide some tentative answers to the questions raised by the impact.

In the first essay, "Liberal Values in the Modern World," C. Wright Mills briefly outlines the fundamental changes that have taken place in Western society, largely as a result of technological changes in the last century. Most importantly, Mills argues that technology has undermined the primary basis of nineteenth-century liberalism, which in turn was the fundamental basis of democratic political institutions and values. Above all, science and technology have led to an increasingly centralized and massive form of production and marketing which has undermined the old system of decentralized entrepreneurial work. Because of these basic changes in our society and their impact, he argues, liberalism has become increasingly irrelevant to what is actually done in our society. While Mills offers few suggestions as to how we might overcome the political crises that have arisen as a result of these changes, he depicts the crises in values very vividly.

In "The Need for a New Political Theory," Lawrence K. Frank picks up where Mills left off. Agreeing with Mills that our historic form of liberalism is no longer tenable, he argues that we must seek to replace the basic ideas that underlay liberalism with ideas about society that are more tenable in a society dominated by science and technology. Above all, he argues that we must develop new social theories which can adequately take into consideration the changing nature of the society and the need to give increasing consideration to the rights of the person, rather than the rights of property emphasized in our historic liberal values.

In "Politics and Technology," Edward T. Chase argues that we are experiencing a continual buildup of fundamental political crisis resulting from the technological changes sweeping our society. Most importantly, he argues, technology has undermined the old free market system assumed by liberal theories and values. It has done this by so increasing the lag time between decision-making and output, and, at the same time, the complexity of decision-making that it is no longer possible for society to rely on the short-run decisions made by consumers in free market situations. The members of our society, especially the political leaders who are in touch with the various scientists and other experts who have analyzed these problems, have come increasingly to recognize that the government at all levels must be involved in supporting longer-run investments than can be supported by free market investments. In fact, the government has long been involved in making precisely such investments in the name of defense and agriculture, and recognizing growing problems, such as the problem of pollution. The government has begun to expand its investment activities into other areas. But as Chase argues, much of this kind of government decision-making and investment has been made on a piecemeal basis. The federal government, and certainly the local governments, have not yet faced up to the basic challenges posed by technologies undermining the free market system. As Chase argues, the challenge can probably only be met by some far more highly developed forms of centralized planning. Only centralized planning can take into consideration all of the complex factors that must be considered if we are to deal adequately with the problems and opportunities posed by the scientific and technological revolution. As he well recognizes, it will not be easy for large segments of American society to accept the values of central planning; yet the problems we are facing, the crises we are facing because we do not have such central planning, are growing so rapidly that even conservative presidential administrations have come to see clearly the need for such central planning. The challenge for our society as a whole will be that of making centralized planning a means of expanding and protecting our individual freedoms while at the same time providing the necessary social coordination of our individual activities. There is no assurance that we can solve the problems involved in achieving both of these at once, but if we do not face the challenge and try to meet it, there is every reason now to expect that we will be faced by growing social chaos that will lead to tyranny as the public seeks in panic to find a way out of the chaos.

C. Wright Mills

LIBERAL VALUES
IN THE MODERN WORLD

Most of us now live as spectators in a world without political interlude: fear of total permanent war stops our kind of morally oriented politics. Our spectatorship means that personal, active experience often seems politically useless and even unreal. This is a time when frustration seems to be in direct ratio to understanding, a time of cultural mediocrity when the levels of public sensibility have sunk below sight. It is a time of irresponsibility, organized and unorganized; when common sense, anchored in fast-outmoded experience has become myopic and irrelevant. Nobody feels secure in a simple place; nobody feels secure and there is no simple place.

It is a time when no terms of acceptance are available, but also no terms of rejection: those on top seem stunned, distracted, and bewildered, and don't know what to do. But what is much more damaging to us: those on the bottom are also without leaders, without counter-ideas, don't know what to do, do not have real demands to make of those in key positions of power.

Whatever the political promises of labor and leftward forces 15 years ago, they have not been fulfilled; whatever leadership they have developed has hidden itself for illusory safety, or been buried by events it neither understands nor wishes to control. Organized labor in the forties and early fifties has been mainly another adaptive and adapting element. What goes on domestically may briefly be described

"Liberal Values in the Modern World" by C. Wright Mills. From Irving Louis Horowitz, ed., Power, Politics and People: The Collected Essays of C. Wright Mills *(New York: Oxford University Press, Inc., 1963), pp. 187–95. Copyright © 1963 by the Estate of C. Wright Mills. Reprinted by permission of the publisher*

in terms of the main drift toward a permanent war economy in a garrison state.

Internationally, of course, the world of nations has been polarized into two deadlocked powers, with no prospects of a structured peace, with a penumbra of variously graded and variously dependent satellites, puppets, and vacuums. For the first time in its easy history, the United States finds itself a nation in a military neighborhood, having common frontiers with a big rival. The United States is a sea and air power from an external position; wherever it turns, it faces a vast land-power with an internal position. In the meantime, Europe has become a virtual colony, held by military force and economic dependence, And neither in the West nor in the East do U.S. spokesmen seem to have ideas and policies that have genuine appeal to the people residing there.

Internationally and domestically, the death of political ideas in the United States coincides with the general intellectual vacuum to underpin our malaise. Insofar as ideas are involved in our political impasse, these ideas center in the nature and present day situation of liberalism. For liberalism is at once the main line of our intellectual heritage and our official political philosophy. I shall not here attempt a full analysis of liberalism's connection with the modern malaise. I only want to lay out some key themes, which I believe must be taken into account in any examination of liberalism today.

I

Like any social philosophy, liberalism can conveniently be understood and discussed: (1) as an articulation of *ideals* which, no matter what its level of generality, operates as a sort of moral optic and set of guidelines for judgments of men, movements and events; (2) as a *theory*, explicit or implied, of how a society works, of its important elements and how they are related, of its key conflicts and how they are resolved; (3) as a social phenomenon, that is, as an *ideology* or political rhetoric—justifying certain institutions and practices, demanding and expecting others. In these terms, what is the situation of liberalism today?

As a set of articulated *ideals*, liberalism has been and is a major part of "the secular tradition of the west." As a political *rhetoric*, liberalism has been the ideology of the rising middle class. As a *theory* of society, liberalism is confined in relevance to the heroic epoch of the middle class. These points are connected, for as a carrier of ideals, liberalism has been detached from any tenable theory of modern society, and however engaging in its received condition, it is no longer a useful guide-line to the future. For the eighteenth and part of the nineteenth centuries, liberal theory did clarify and offer insight; for the twentieth century, it just as often confuses.

II

Liberalism, as a set of ideals, is still viable, and even compelling to Western men. That is one reason why it has become a common denominator of American political rhetoric; but there is another reason. The ideals of liberalism have been divorced from any realities of modern social structure that might serve as the means of their realization. Everybody can easily agree on general ends; it is more difficult to agree on means and the relevance of various means to the ends articulated. The detachment of liberalism from the facts of a going society make it an excellent mask for those who do not, cannot, or will not do what would have to be done to realize its ideals.

As a kind of political rhetoric, liberalism has been banalized: now it is commonly used by everyone who talks in public for every divergent and contradictory purpose. Today we hear liberals say that one liberal can be "for," and another liberal "against," a vast range of contradictory political propositions. What this means is that liberalism as a common denominator of American political rhetoric, is without coherent content; that, in the process of its banalization, its goals have been so formalized as to provide no clear moral optic. The crisis of liberalism (and of American political reflection) is due to liberalism's success in becoming the official language for all public statement. To this fact was added its use in the New Deal Era when, in close contact with power, liberalism became administrative. Its crisis in lack of clarity is underpinned by its use by all interests, classes, and parties.

It is in this situation that professional liberals sometimes make a fetish of indecision, which they would call open-mindedness, as against inflexibility; of the absence of criteria, which they would call tolerance, as against dogmatism; of the formality and hence political irrelevance of criteria, which they would call "speaking broadly," as against "details."

We may not, of course, dismiss liberalism merely because it is a common denominator of political rhetoric. Its wide use as justification limits the choices and, to some extent, guides the decisions of those in authority. For if it is the common denominator, all powerful decisions made in the open must be justified in its terms, and this may restrain the deciders even if they do not "believe in it." For men are influenced in their use of authority by the rhetoric they feel they must employ. The leaders as well as the led, and even the myth-makers, are influenced by prevailing rhetorics of justification.

Liberals have repeatedly articulated a secular humanism, stressing the priceless value of the individual personality, and the right of each individual to be dealt with in accordance with rational and understandable laws, to which all power is also subject. They have been humanist in the sense that they see man as the measure of all things: policies and events are good or bad in terms of their effect on men; institutions and societies are to be judged in terms of what they mean to and for the individual human being. Liberals have assumed that men should control their own life-fates. It is in terms of this value that the entire concern with consent to authority and the opposition to violence should be understood. All loyalties to specific movements and organizations tend, for the liberal, to be conditional upon his own principles, rather than blindly to an organization. Liberals have assumed that there are rational ways to acquire knowledge, and that substantive reason, anchored in the individual, provides the way out.

As a set of such ideals, liberalism has very heavily contributed to the big tradition of the West, but it is not the sole carrier of this tradition; it is not to be identified with it. And it is a real question whether today it is the most whole-hearted carrier of it, for it is to be greatly doubted that, as a theory of society, liberalism is in a position to lead or help men carry these ideals into realization.

So, if as ideal, liberalism is the secular tradition of the West, as a theory of society, which enables these ideals, it is the ideology of one class inside one epoch. If the moral force of liberalism is still stimulating, its sociological content is weak; it has no theory of society adequate to its moral aims.

III

The assumptions of liberal theories about society, have to do with how liberal values could be anchored, with how they could operate as guide to policy. The liberal ideals of the eighteenth and nineteenth centuries were anchored in several basic assumptions about the condition of modern society that are no longer simple or clear:

(i) Liberalism has assumed that both freedom and security, its key values, flourish in a world of small entrepreneurs. But it is quite clear that one of the most decisive changes over the last hundred years is the enormous increase in the scale of property units. This has meant that the ideals of liberty and of security have changed: absolute liberty to control property has become tyranny. The meaning of freedom, positively put, has to be restated now, not as independence, but as control over that upon which the individual is dependent. Security, once resting on the small holding, has become, in the world of large property, anxiety—anxiety produced by the concentration of process and by the manner of living without expectation of owning. Positively, security must be group-guaranteed; individual men can no longer provide for their own futures.

If a particular ideal of freedom assumes for its realization the dominance of a scatter of small property, then, the social meaning of this ideal is quite different from a statement of freedom that assumes a situation of concentrated property. It is in its theory of society, tacit or explicit, that we find the political content of a social philosophy. If men assume the dominance of huge-scale property, and yet state eighteenth-century ideals, they are off base. In the kindergarten of political philosophy one learns that the idea of freedom *in general* is more serviceable as politically irrelevant rhetoric than ideal. Twentieth-century problems cannot be solved by eighteenth-century phrases. Liberty is not **an** a-priori individual fact, and it has been a social achievement only when liberal ideals have fortunately coincided with social realities.

Order can be reconciled with liberty by an underlying common sentiment, or by a balance of harmoniously competing groups. Common sentiment can grow from slow-paced tradition or be imposed from a powerful center. Competitive balance can be maintained only if each faction remains small enough and equal enough to compete freely. But now there is no common sentiment, and there is no balance, but a lop-sided competition between and among dominant factions and midget interests.

Liberalism, in the nineteenth-century epoch of its triumph, never really took into account the changing economic foundations of the political ideals and forms it espoused. That simple fact goes far to explain the decline of liberalism in authoritative cogency. This is the fact upon which Marxism has been correctly focused and upon which it has capitalized.

(ii) Many classic liberals, perhaps especially of the Rousseauian and Jeffersonian persuasion, have assumed the predominance of rural or "small city states," in brief, of a small-scale community. Liberal discussion of the general will, and liberal notions of "public opinion" usually rest on such assumptions. We no longer live in this sort of small-scale world.

(iii) A third assumption about society, characteristic of classic liberalism, has been the stress upon the autonomy of different institutional orders. In the beginning, as with Locke, it would split off religious institutions from the political, so that the political justifications, whatever they may be, had to be secular. Later on, the economic order was split from the political order, in the classic case of laissez-faire, perhaps coming to a head in the early philosophical radicals in England. But that was not the end of making different institutional orders autonomous. The kinship order was also to be split from the other orders so that there was a free marriage market, just as there was a free commodity market.

Moreover, in each of these orders a similar principle was upheld: that of individual freedom of choice—as an economic agent; as a presumptuous political man, who had to be shown before he would obey; as a man on the marriage market making a free contract with his partner; and so on.

But what has happened is the fusion of several institutional orders; the co-ordination of the major orders has become the contemporary reality. We see in the United States today an increased coincidence and fusion of the economic, political, and military orders.

(iv) A fourth underlying sociological assumption, probably the most subtle and far-reaching, certainly the most philosophically relevant, is that the individual is the seat of rationality. When liberals speak of rationality and "the increase of enlightenment," they have assumed that the individual will be increased in stature and dignity because *his* power to reason and *his* knowledge will be increased. But the decisive fact here, as signified quite well by such writers as Max Weber and Karl Mannheim, is that the seat of rationality has shifted from the individual and is now in the big institution. The increase of enlightenment does not necessarily wise up the individual. This has to do with the distinction of substantative from formal rationality, in short, the growth of a bureaucratic organization of knowledge. The prevailing character as well as the distribution of rationality now leads to a whole set of questions to which we have no contemporary liberal answers. This modern weakness and irrationality of the individual, and especially his political apathy, is crucial for liberalism; for liberalism has classically relied on the reasoning individual as its lever for progressive change.

(v) Tied in with the belief in the growth of the individual's substantive rationality is the belief in the explicitness of authority. Men, as individuals or as groups of individuals, could learn to know who exercised power and so could debate it or obey. But today, one of the crucial political problems "for experts," as for laymen, is to locate exactly who has the power.

It is fashionable now, especially among those who have left what radical circles remain, to suppose that "there is no ruling class," just as it was fashionable in the thirties to suppose a set of class villains to be the source of all social injustice and public malaise. I should be as far from supposing that some enemy could be firmly located, that some one or two set of men were responsible, as I should be from supposing that it is all merely impersonal, tragic drift. The view that all is blind drift is largely a fatalist projection of one's own feeling of impotence and perhaps a salve of guilt about it. The view that all is due to the conspiracy of an easily locatable enemy is also a hurried projection from the difficult effort to understand how structural shifts open opportunities to various elites and how various elites take advantage or fail to take advantage of them. To accept either view is to relax the effort rationally to understand in detail how it is.

There are obviously gradations of power and opportunities among modern populations, which is not to say that all ruling powers are united, or that they fully know what they do, or that they are consciously joined in conspiracy. One can, however, be more concerned with their structural position and the consequences of their decisive actions than with the extent of their awareness or the impurity of their motives. But such analysis has not been part of the liberal tradition, nor does this tradition provide decisive help in undertaking it.

IV

The root problem of any "democratic" or "liberal"—or even humanist—ideals is that they are in fact statements of hope or demands or preferences of an intellectual elite psychologically capable of individually fulfilling them, but they are projected for a population which in the twentieth century is not at present capable of fulfilling them.

What is inferred from this depends, in part, upon what is seen to be the causes of this mass incapability, and, in part, simply upon the degree of sanguinity. In nineteenth-century liberalism, the causes were seen largely as ignorance; so the answer was education. This was true of classic liberalism and, in part, of classic socialism, although the meaning and the further reasons for ignorance were more sophisticatedly worked out by socialist than by liberal writers. In the twentieth century, serious thinkers have further developed this socialist view, whether or not they know it as socialist, and have come to see that the whole structure of modern society, in particular its bureaucratic and communication systems virtually expropriate from all but a small intellectual elite the capacity for individual freedom in any adequate psychological meaning of the term.

The intellectual question for liberals, then, rests on the confrontation of the old individual ideals with new social and psychological facts. The old social anchors of individual freedom and individual security of small scattered properties and small-scale communities are gone; the roots of these values in autonomously operating institutions are dried up; the seat of rationality is no longer unambiguously the individual; the centers of power are as often hidden as explicit. And so the question becomes whether the ideals themselves must be given up or drastically revised, or whether there are ways of re-articulating them that retain their old moral force in a world that moral liberals never made.

Lawrence K. Frank

THE NEED FOR A
NEW POLITICAL THEORY

We urgently need a new political theory to replace that which was formulated in the late-eighteenth century and has become cumulatively inadequate and frustrating for the present and an impediment to the future. Such a revised political theory will be a necessity for the cultural renewal we must undertake, as well as a statement of policy for guiding our new proposals.

In 1776 and the period preceding the establishment of the United States, the founding fathers, hoping to establish a new nation and inaugurate a new social order, sought promising ideas and conceptual formulations for what they desired to achieve. The government they proposed was oriented to the protection of private property, the adjudication of disputes, the collection of customs, the conduct of foreign affairs, and the maintenance of national defense. They found authority for this in John Locke's theory of representative government and a model in a similar tri-party division of government that the British had earlier tried and abandoned. They were persuaded by the eighteenth-century belief in the rationality of man and accepted proposals that emphasized the individual's capacity for acting rationally in pursuing his own self-interest and happiness, calculating his prospective gains and losses.

But the basic foundation for these proposals was the conception of society as a superhuman organization, operated and kept in balance by immense superhuman forces, like the celestial machinery of

"The Need for a New Political Theory" by Lawrence K. Frank. From Daedalus (Summer 1967): 177–84. Reprinted by permission of Daedalus, Journal of the American Academy of Arts and Sciences.

Newton from which this model was derived. These forces were operated to maintain the new nation in its appointed orbit.

This well-known history of the country is rehearsed here to remind us how a political theory became directive and gave rise to a new society. It was translated not only into a governmental organization and administration but also into what may be called the philosophy of American life—a flexible guide as to what individuals, groups, and organizations could and should do. Especially we should recognize that government is not to be conceived as inherent in or derived from nature, nor as an expression of natural law but as a humanly created institution, carried on by the individuals who have adopted its aims and practices and accepted the political theory that has rationalized and justified what they do.

Since 1900 we have experienced several major alterations in our society, some of which are truly radical changes. Thus, we have had a rapidly enlarging population with a changing age distribution and made up of a variety of ethnic-cultural groups. We have also had a biological revolution, marked by the prolongation of life and the emergence of old-age groups that are actively forming associations and pressing for their own advantage and protection. We have also had an urban revolution characterized not only by the increasing population of cities, but by basic changes in our former ways of living. Earlier, many were engaged in *making* a living on the farm where the "extended" family exerted as a more or less self-sufficient household their skills, foresight, strength, and endurance in wresting a living from the soil. Today, no urban resident nor "nuclear" family can make a living; each must try to *earn* a living, or otherwise obtain income, for rent, the purchase of food and clothing, and the many recurrent expenditures that have become customary, if not necessary, for city living.

Many are seeking compensation and protection, exhibiting their inability to be independent. They are also hoping to overcome the loss of the "belonging" once enjoyed from shared beliefs and loyalties, from one's family and kinship ties, from having a place in the community, and from religious affiliations. They are now seeking collective status, relinquishing or greatly curtailing their power of individual contracting. Instead of bargaining individually, they now look to membership in organizations to which they surrender the power of contract for the status they gain as members. These organizations "bargain collectively" for their members, as we see not only in labor unions but in professional and educational associations, in religious and other organizations. Especially important are the corporations, which are empowered by their owners-stockholders to manage their property, to enter into contracts and other agreements on their behalf in the expectation of profits.

Political parties with their hierarchical organization not only offer opportunities for enhancing status but also provide rewards and special jobs to their loyal members who are unable to attain equivalent compensations and salaries except by patronage. Status fosters what we call "featherbedding." Not limited to labor unions and political parties, featherbedding is widely practiced in many organizations in business and finance, government and the military, religious institutions and, not infrequently, the helping professions and service institutions. Those who belong are rewarded for little or no work, except what they are told not to do or to say. Many special privileges are, however, also granted to individuals because they have a legalized status, because they belong to a special class—such as age and sex groups, the handicapped, the retarded, and the mentally disturbed. Their deviant status entitles them to allowance and protection.

These and other changes illustrate a shift in our traditional emphasis upon the rights and protection of property to an increasing recognition of the rights of persons; from the doctrine of equality of opportunity to the emerging conception of the equality of human needs, not only for the "creature comforts" but also for the dignity and integrity of the individual and family that are continually jeopardized and denied by the persistence of anachronistic beliefs, practices, and laws. There have been a number of expressions of this shift and changing evaluation. The New Deal, which enlarged governmental services and financial support, was followed by the New Frontier, and now by the Great Society programs. Although these slogans have evoked support for often reluctantly adopted measures, they have not been productive of a new political theory rationalizing these departures from our accepted beliefs about the limited powers and responsibilities of government.

The political theories and governmental authority derived from theology are still being reiterated on public occasions, but they no longer have their former meaning nor provide the authority for governmental action. The separation of church and state is being decided not so much by legislation and court decisions, but by the changes in individual beliefs, expectations, and loyalties fostered by governmental intervention in private affairs.

The Federal Government now provides a wide range of professional and technical assistance, with many direct subsidies and special tax allowances and concessions to business, finance, industry, transportation, and communication—indeed, to the whole range of free enterprise. This assistance to private business has been explained and justified as promoting prosperity and advancing the national welfare. But assistance and services to individuals and families have been strongly resisted and only reluctantly provided since there is no adequate rationalization for such extensions of government activities. The need for a political theory for this emerging "Service State" is, therefore, especially urgent.

The Service State, not to be confused with the Welfare State with its aura of charity and philanthropy, is oriented to the enhanced "well-being" of everyone, as Halbert Dunn has expressed it. It marks the acceptance of human conservation as the basic democratic task; each year sees the enlargement and extension of services furnished directly or financed by the Federal Government and reinforced by state and local agencies. These services embrace medical and health care, improved housing and urban rehabilitation, educational facilities and programs from early childhood into adult years, plus the improved care and support of the indigent, the handicapped, the impaired, and all others incapable of fending for themselves in our money economy.

Each addition and enlargement is made as a separate program with no coherent and systematic commitment, no political theory to justify and rationalize these enlarged government activities, and no statement of policy for their extension and administration. We are improvising and operating by a series of piecemeal programs.

As Julius A. Stratton pointed out in his Commencement Address at M.I.T. in June, 1964:

> Our efforts must now move to a higher plateau. We can no longer afford to nibble away piece by piece at the problems of the modern city—of transportation—of underdeveloped economies—of automation—or of disarmament. . . . Our ailments are vast and complex, and they will yield only to planned collaborative attacks focused on clear objectives and leading to concerted action.[1]

This implies the need for an over-all, comprehensive policy that will assert the criteria for choices and decisions. With a clear statement of policy, those who make social decisions can be guided, as if by "an unseen hand," when exercising their autonomy to integrate their efforts by collaborating with others who are responsive to these

1. Julius A. Stratton, "Commencement Address, Massachusetts Institute of Technology, *Daedalus*, Vol. 3, No. 4 (Fall, 1964), p. 1242.

same criteria. Without a statement of basic criteria for national policies, the various specialized programs and the separately located authority of governments and private agencies will continue to plan and execute their separate and often irreconcilable programs.

For a free society, therefore, we need the guidance of basic principles and especially a political theory congruous with and appropriate to the new requirements and opportunities of today. Where can we look for guidance and fruitful direction for a new political theory? Following the example of the founding fathers, we might seek in science for the reorientation we need; we must realize, however, that they did not attempt to apply the Newtonian methods and techniques for mathematical reasoning. Nor did they rely upon empirical research and demand quantitative findings to decide what was desirable and feasible. They did not believe that they were bound by existing trends, especially since they were determined to interrupt so much of the customary uses and the prevailing practices of their time. They were concerned with innovation, with the establishment of a new social order and a new kind of government that would express and make possible the attainment of the values they cherished.

Accordingly, we should not look hopefully to the bewildering array of contemporary findings and research techniques nor try to invoke science as the source of our procedure, but, rather, attempt to understand and apply some of the recently developed concepts and assumptions—the new ways of creative thinking and theoretical formulation—that seem relevant and promising. Also, we might employ some of the newly-developed conceptual models that may be useful for a new political theory.

Social problems, unlike scientific problems generated by theoretical implications and curiosity about natural events, rise from the inadequacies and conflicts in a social order, especially from the neglect or refusal to revise anachronistic and obsolete institutions and practices so that we can cope with urgent human needs and better express our aspirations.

An analytic approach to problems fragments what is an organized complexity calling for the study of the whole. A fruitful concept of such a whole is that of an "open system," as contrasted to a "closed system" that can be isolated like laboratory preparations and rigidly controlled experiments, excluding all inputs except those to be explored as selected variables or isolable "mechanisms."

As Ludwig Bertalanffy has pointed out, open systems operate with continual inputs and outputs, with unceasing functioning, and with ever-changing states, and are therefore not subject to the classical controls and to attempted replication of findings.[2] Open systems—embracing organisms, personalities, human institutions, social orders, and cultures—can be and are frequently studied analytically to disclose selected dimensions or variables, but these yield what might be called "scientific artifacts" that ignore the complex inter-relationships and unceasing communication of the open systems they investigate. The components and participants in open systems are closely coupled and entrained, communicating with the environing world and evoking feedbacks for their direction and stabilization. Unlike the physical-chemical elements and their unchanging properties, open systems and their components can and do change, as the evolution of organisms and the development of cultures, social orders, and changing governments notably demonstrate.

Another fruitful approach has been provided by cybernetics as formulated by the late Norbert Wiener. Cybernetics has frequently been misused by wrongly applying it to static entities and inertial systems. Likewise, feedbacks have been frequently misinterpreted as externally-applied forces; they should be seen as what the system, organism, or machine evokes from the environment for correction and direction and generates internally for its co-ordinated functioning.

Especially noteworthy and promising is the concept of self-organizing systems. "Hard-nosed" scientists and engineers are increasingly accepting and working with this seemingly teleological concept, as is shown by the papers in *Principles of Self-Organizing Systems,* edited by Heinz von Foerster and G. W. Zopf, Jr.[3] These papers emphasize that systems are not only self-organizing, but also self-directing and self-stabilizing, and may to a considerable extent be self-repairing and capable of goal-seeking, purposive behavior.

These recent concepts, explored and elaborated upon by a number of scientists from different disciplines, have proved to be highly productive. W. Ross Ashby has proposed that a system be viewed as composed of a number of sub-systems, each of which has its own range of fluctuation; when the system receives an impact, one or more of the sub-systems can "roll with the punches" and thereby maintain the stability of the total system. When, however, one or more of these sub-systems are required to operate beyond their normal range of

2. Ludwig Bertalanffy, "The Theory of Open Systems in Physics and Biology," *Science,* Vol. 3 (1950), pp. 27–29; "General Systems Theory," *Human Biology,* Vol. 23, No. 4 (December, 1951); "General Systems Theory: A New Approach to Unity of Science," *Human Biology,* Vol. 28, No. 4 (December, 1956).

3. Heinz von Foerster and G. W. Zopf, Jr., eds., *Principles of Self-Organizing Systems* (London, 1962).

variability, the whole system undergoes what Ashby calls a "step function" and shifts to a "new track," changing its former operations and functioning. Any marked change in one function or operation of a system usually involves alteration and compensatory changes in the whole system because each component of a sub-system is interrelated to the others.

As a result of these recent approaches, there is a growing realization that the familiar statement "the whole is greater than the sum of its parts" is misleading and invalid when applied to social organizations. This axiom assumes that the "parts" are more or less homogeneous units that can be aggregated and added as a quantitative ensemble. But the so-called "parts" of a system or organization are its highly differentiated components and participants, each of which has specialized but coupled activities whereby the whole is generated and maintained.

We have no adequate conception of such a dynamic organization. Traditionally, organization has been conceived of as a hierarchical entity and illustrated by charts with a chain of command from the top to the lower echelons and individuals. Some definitions are offered as static models that are supposed to operate, but there is no clearly stated theory of how they work. Today we are beginning to recognize that organisms and human organizations are persistent configurations of functioning processes closely coupled and entrained and engaged in circular, reciprocal operations involving feedbacks.

A promising model for a political theory is that of a communications network, with many different channels for transmitting a variety of messages. This social communications network cannot be encompassed by "Information Theory" and its mathematical elaboration, devised initially for coded verbal messages. The social communications network transmits many different messages of social symbols that we call political, economic, social, religious, and so on. These group-sanctioned symbols are used by individuals and groups in the continuous transactions and negotiations of social life. This model offers a possibility for unifying now separate social sciences and relinquishing what each of them assumes to be a discrete system with its own "forces" and theoretical interpretation. Instead of the assumption of great superhuman forces or coercive trends, we may find clues to the dynamics of social operations and changes in the human behavior exhibited in social symbols. Appropriate patterns of behavior may give rise to the recurrent regularities of a social order and also generate the trends and the innovations in all our institutions and customary practices.

Unless we are persuaded, as many are, that our lives are determined by inexorable natural laws, divine ordination, or coercive trends, that we must accept as our fate and "drear our weird," as the Scots say, we cannot avoid much longer the recognition that we live by and for what we believe, value, and aspire to, and that these beliefs must be translated into the choices and decisions that guide our individual and group living.

These concepts appear to be highly relevant and appropriate to the modern political theory for a social order undergoing rapid and, at present, unco-ordinated changes. They are especially applicable to our social order because they emphasize how the whole of our society is disturbed by separate and unco-ordinated attempts at revision that so often ignore their inextricable relation to the larger system. Moreover, these new concepts of a system show that the classical assumptions about social order must be replaced since we can no longer think of society as an inertial system governed by large-scale social forces, a surviving eighteenth-century metaphor that is widely accepted and used by social scientists and by the public.

Alfred North Whitehead pointed out some years ago that "those societies which cannot combine reverence for their symbols with freedom for their revision must ultimately decay, either from anarchy or the slow atrophy by useless shadows." A social order that cannot reaffirm its aspirations, goals, values and also revise and reconstruct its institutions must succumb to increasing disorder and conflict or decline as the torch of human advance is taken over by the new nations.

Edward T. Chase

POLITICS AND TECHNOLOGY

At last there is a dawning realization that in the United States
it is rapid technological change rather than ideological strife or even
economics that is building up a fundamental political crisis. This
realization is evidenced in several recent symposiums involving a
number of the outstanding thinkers of the times and by recent executive acts and legislation with far-reaching implications. What is
happening is that technology's effects are suddenly calling into question the viability of our political institutions to a degree unknown
at least since the Civil War.

There is a growing awareness that tomorrow's political convulsion
will be different from what doctrinaires, obsessed with dated rhetoric
about socialism vs. capitalism, have led us to expect, because it derives
from the cumulative impact of technology, an impact that is impersonal, nonideological, relentless, and possibly overwhelming. Above
all else our political adaptability and inventiveness are being challenged by technology. This point has seldom been demonstrated more
dramatically than by last summer's Senate filibuster growing out of
the dispute over whether AT&T or the government should dominate
the control of the communications space satellite. Such perplexity and
passion were fomented by the power problem created by this particular technological triumph as to immobilize the political process for
days, until cloture was invoked in the Senate for the first time in 35
years.

Examples of political consternation provoked by technology are becoming pervasive. They range from the familiar to the esoteric. How, for instance, does a free society force human and land resources out of agriculture to adjust to the realities of modern scientific farming? And does a free society make the massive, explosive problem of retraining workers displaced by automation the responsibility of state governments or the national government or industry, or some ingenious combination of all? Again, when technological unemployment in combination with scientific medicine produces a growing population of "retired" elderly persons in an urbanized, wage-based industrial society, how will their heavy medical costs for the inevitable chronic ills of old age be financed? Or when an essential public service is threatened with extinction as a paying proposition, owing to fatal competition from more advanced technology, is the government helpless, as in the case of the New Haven Railroad, or will our political leaders devise some successful expedient without incurring a constitutional crisis? Again, is our incapacity to adjust politically such that we must forego manifest social gains from technological progress—as almost happened in the Hanford, Washington, atomic power plant case, where an invaluable supply of reactor-generated steam for creating electricity would have been wasted had there not been an eleventh hour political resolution of the conflict between private and government ownership? When completed in 1965, this will be the world's largest nuclear power plant. The plant will be the locus of further political controversy soon over the question of what particular industries the electric power will be used for. Use in one category of industry will result in 5,000 new jobs; use in another in 10,000 new jobs; and in still another category 36,000 new jobs. Not the "market" but a conscious deliberation by officials will resolve the issue.

This Hanford example, like the communications space satellite debate, introduces problems with political implications of a new order of complexity for American society. Yet already it is being widely sensed that they are only the beginning. To be sure, man has long had to make gradual social adaptation to technological change. It is the exponential rate of change today that is uniquely challenging to our political superstructure.

What is perhaps most conducive to political controversy is the fact that advancing technology is beginning to promise immediate practical solutions to hitherto insoluble frustrations, if it is given the chance. As a practical matter there must first be expensive studies of the feasibility of technological innovations and then funds appropriated for research and development. If, as is increasingly the case, these funds must be substantial and there is no promise of relatively quick profit, then the market mechanism simply does not become engaged. Only the government can undertake the enterprise. It is true that in a modern mixed economy this does not invariably create a political dilemma. But in the United States it does more frequently than not. There may be no immediate political repercussions from the unusual amount of attention President Kennedy has been giving to conquering the problem of turning brackish and sea water into usable water. Seventy-five million dollars is being spent by the Office of Saline Water to ascertain the best of a number of competing commercial processes. Nor would there be a formidable political problem in governmental support, say, for eradicating malaria from the world (3 million deaths annually, 300 million people afflicted), which is something distinctly within reach at a cost of only $50 million spread over a ten-year period.

But consider the political reverberations should the government undertake the rescue operation that could be consummated for our moribund textile industry if technology were subsidized—as is being seriously considered in Washington—to master the task of applying high speed electronic computers to our textile looms, thus rendering American textiles competitive in the world market. Comparable practical achievements are within reach in a score of areas, were it not for the political obstacles—for instance, the revival of our East Coast shipping industry by the use of fast hydrofoil ships now anchored on drawing boards for lack of developmental money, ships quite capable of out-performing trucks (hence offering some relief to the traffic problem); or, for another example, creating a major new source of high protein food by making a systematic effort to harvest the ocean.

The questions posed by these considerations are ultimately and essentially political. They go to the heart of the political problem of how a democratic government, one that is both responsive and responsible, reconciles technological promise with the will of the public. For decisions have to be made as to what public resources are to be devoted to what technological ventures—and who is to make the choice. Throughout the lifetime of the United States, our tradition has been to depend upon the market mechanism to register the people's choices. It is the doctrine of consumer sovereignty, the revered "invisible hand" (which economist Robert Heilbroner usefully characterizes as a system "to mobilize and allocate human energies and to distribute the social produce in a manner to assure society of its continued existence"). However, the evidence is now becoming overwhelming that the traditional market mechanism of supply and demand, for all its uncanny power to articulate the public will, simply is not up to reflecting the long-range values that have to be weighed if a rational use is to be made of the new technology. The point is that this is not a doctrinaire matter, a sly triumph by creeping socialists; it is a result of technological change.

The underlying dilemma arises from the fact that a democratic government must be responsive to the present electorate, yet, since it makes decisions that determine the impact of technology upon the environment of succeeding generations, it must also be responsive to future electorates. Government is now facing situations with increasing frequency where currently popular practices sanctioned by the market system (exploitation of natural resources is an obvious example) must be modified for the sake of this future. Rachel Carson's *Silent Spring*, about the devastating ecological impact of pesticides, has wonderfully dramatized this issue.

This is to put the matter negatively, however. The political problem is not so much a matter of placing restraints on technology. It stems more from the fact that positive forces are now building up that urge us to circumvent the market mechanism and apply public funds directly to technology, as traditionally we have done only in wartime. What is slowly being realized is that the support of technology cannot any longer be confined to what the public wants. After all, the public can only choose alternatives among things it knows; it simply does not know enough to project its wants into the future, with the result that the market mechanism cannot be depended upon to nourish technological development. For the first time in our history the government has set up a unit, called the Panel on Civilian Technology, responsive to this fact. This little-known operation was established strictly for the purpose of encouraging technological innovation on the premise that new technology, as much as or more than new plant and equipment investment, is what stimulates economic growth. The 18-man panel, composed of industrialists, academics, and bureaucrats, is especially concerned with four industries suffering from technological lag—textiles, coal, housing, and transport. It reports to science adviser Jerome Wiesner, to economic adviser Walter Heller, and to Commerce Secretary Luther Hodges. It has already become a center of controversy in certain planning circles because of its first report, on urban transportation, in which it argues against support for rail transit and instead favors express buses on exclusive rights of way.

The political inhibitions to direct government subsidy on any substantial scale remain enormous, of course. Suggestions such as those made at a Brookings Institution symposium on "The Uses of Economics"—suggestions for revitalizing our lagging economy by having the government finance research and development in areas like communications, transport, food, and industrial production—are still widely judged as heresy. In business circles they are viewed as the sure road to Communist despotism.

"To what extent should government finance or subsidize industrial research in general, or for certain industries as it has already done so productively for agriculture and defense?" asked Charles J. Hitch, former Chairman of the Research Council of the RAND corporation, at the Brookings meeting. Now an Assistant Secretary of Defense, Hitch went on to say that "relatively small expenditures" for deliberately planned research and development in the military sector "have been staggeringly, alarmingly, productive. . . . I have tried to think of any reasons why the military area should be unique in this respect; I can think of none. That it is not is suggested by our somewhat similar experience in agriculture, though on a much smaller scale. I suspect that there has been a serious misallocation of resources and that it corresponds to economists' misallocation of their effort between problems of investment and problems of technological change." Coming from so highly placed a representative of the power elite, these are words calculated to give pause. Hitch was impressively seconded in his main sentiments by Francis M. Bator, of M.I.T., whose cool disparagement of laissez-faire markets as an effective allocator of resources went unchallenged.

A fruitful way to gain a perspective on the force-feeding of technology by government is to recall the attitude of the ancient Greeks toward science. They viewed science as sacred knowledge. And, since the Greek city states placed a premium upon political and social stability, the esoteric knowledge of science, the secret of manipulating nature, was confined to the few so as to preclude the social and political disruptions bound to follow in the wake of any widespread applications of technology. Everything had to be secondary to the ideal of a stable social order.

Now between this attitude and the modern American attitude the contrast is extreme. Our operating assumption has been that the essence of the free society is to encourage the unfettered intelligence and to accept all discoveries and their applications. Whether this attitude can be maintained is beginning to be insistently questioned today for the first time. Is our capacity for political inventiveness equal to the challenge of devising new political forms, alignments, and procedures that can deal effectively with technology and simultaneously preserve democratic vitality? In three recent symposiums organized independently of one another and along quite different lines, one in Santa Barbara, another in Boston, and the third at Arden House, Harriman, New York, the common subject was the social impact of new technology. These were three highly instructive sessions, illuminating many of the conundrums under scrutiny here. The imperative but largely unanswered question that eventually emerged in all these meetings was the question of *political* control, with special emphasis upon the relations between the private sector and government.

One might assume that there is already a substantial literature on technology's impact on politics. To be sure, there are numerous allusions to it in the late-blooming literature about the changes technology has brought about in social and cultural relations (though not even a professional journal on this subject existed until 1958, when *Technology and Culture* was founded). But there are no full-scale treatments of the specifically political relationship. Economist Heilbroner (at the Arden House meeting) noted that "the steady invasion of technology is the commanding reality that shapes the economic relation of man to nature in our day; how extraordinary, then, that the two most important economists of fullblown capitalism, Alfred Marshall and Lord Keynes, have virtually nothing to say about the impact of technology on the economic system!" No doubt the key to the absence of a literature on the impact of technology on politics is due to the fact that political structure is essentially reactive to economic forces, and only lately has there even been any explicit acknowledgment of technology's undermining of the market system.

In any event, the division of opinion over the fundamentally political problem of whether man does or even can control technology became sharp and even impassioned in these symposiums. Lewis Mumford produced a characteristically eloquent paper for the Santa Barbara meeting pleading for the precedence of humanist direction. Wrote Mumford: "The quantitative over-production of both material and intellectual goods poses, immediately for the Western World, ultimately for all mankind, a new problem: the problem of regulation, distribution, assimilation, integration, teleological direction." In Mumford's view, "The most dangerous notion an age of automation can entertain is the belief that machines have goals of their own, to which man must submit if he knows what's best for him." His colleague at Santa Barbara, author and scientist Sir Robert Watson-Watt, echoed this with the words, "There can, in fact, be no more disastrous undermining of the human condition than that of regarding technology as a self-propagated, self-propelled entity not fully controllable by the appropriately designed agencies of the body politic."

The University of Bordeaux's Jacques Ellul, the chief spokesman at the Santa Barbara symposium for the view that man really no longer has any control over technology, caricatured the humanists in this passage from his hotly discussed paper: "An idea frequently to be encountered in superficial inquiries concerning Technique (technology) is the following: 'At bottom everything depends on the way Technique is employed; mankind has only to use Technique for the good and avoid using it for the bad.'" Ellul's paper is a demonstration of the, to him, impossible task of discerning the ultimate effects of technology and hence of bringing it under effective rational control. He contends that control eludes us because we never can foresee all the consequences of a given technological innovation.

The project that seems to have excited the chief alarm among the Santa Barbara participants is "Operation Chariot," the Atomic Energy Commission's plan to build a harbor by an atomic explosion. Professor Ritchie Calder of Edinburgh cited this project as exemplifying the demonic tendency of technology. It carries man along with it at a furious, mindless pace, unchecked because the public is ignorant of the full results of the project. Calder recoils at the prospect of what he calls "pseudo-technologists" such as the Atomic Energy Commission making decisions, since they have vested interests in the very technology they should be helping us to control. Calder speaks of humanity being at the mercy of "the faceless men at the elbow of the uninformed." Professor Richard L. Meier of Michigan, a specialist in resource conservation, takes comfort in his belief that there are at least 500 people of Ph.D. level in government bureaucracies dedicated to preventing the misuse of technology. The "throttling process" they carry on suppresses the bad ideas like "Operation Chariot." Professor Melvin Kranzberg contended that the fact that the RAND Corporation has been asked by the Pentagon to study the social implications of technology is most encouraging. Robert M. Hutchins, never one to suffer facile optimism gladly, complained that although the difficulties for humanity if technology is not controlled had been made clear enough, no one had yet succeeded in outlining a program for control "which would not be subject to the charge that it might be worse for the human race than technology unchecked."

Between the pessimists and the optimists it is possible to identify a pragmatic bridge or middle position. It has nowhere been better exemplified than in comments by Columbia philosopher Charles Frankel made at the 1961 National Conference on Social Welfare. Frankel takes off from the premise that "the justification of a system of decentralized capitalist competition is that it energizes and makes possible the spirit of invention and innovation. That system seems to be working very well and as a result not only do we have technological unemployment *but we can count on it as a normal feature and sign that our system is doing well.* It is the price we pay for our success, the inevitable defect that goes with our virtue."

Frankel does not say we can foresee all the consequences of technological innovation. But he does say we have known for some time now that the social impact of technology is dislocating, and therefore we should not panic, treating the dislocations as an "accident," as "something that shouldn't happen." Instead, we should deliberately establish permanent preventive institutions carefully designed to cope with such dislocations as we can anticipate. In this instance his concern was with technological disemployment, and he called for retraining and relocation agencies not created in an *"ad hoc* and retrospective basis" but as standing agencies no less a permanent and fully articulated part of our institutional framework than our school systems.

An effort along these lines is getting under way with the launching of the Manpower Development and Training Act under the newly created Office of Manpower, Automation and Training. It is one of the most significant pieces of legislation in recent years, since for the first time it establishes the national government's responsibility for the reemployment of a labor force wracked by technological change. Not only does this act provide for $435 millions over three years to retrain 400,000 of the hard core unemployed; it marks the advent of a Federal program that manpower experts in Washington say will have no end because so rapid is the pace of technology that workers must anticipate new jobs in new industries perhaps a half-dozen different times in their working lives. As (then) Labor Secretary Arthur Goldberg observed of it, "For the first time in our history we are setting out to make opportunity a matter of design, and not chance." In the Congressional hearings on the law, conservative critics expressed anxiety that this was the beginning of an unprecedented control over the nation's manpower by the central government. The law does in fact mean that a government functionary and not the individual retrainee determines what skill the latter is to be taught. It is decided on the basis of known manpower needs and on a judgment of the retrainee's potential.

Frankel's paradoxical plea is for energetic centralized planning for the express purpose of avoiding political despotism. Such planning, says Frankel, must be shaped by the goal of lessening the inevitable disruptive impact of technology and the resultant pressure for political relief through oppressively authoritarian measures. "The pressures toward centralization in our society are very great," he stated. "Without deliberate planning at the center they are going to become greater. The policies of dealing with emergencies, of creating *ad hoc* measures for problem after problem, multiply restrictions, regulations, laws and inhibitions on human energy. People misunderstand the true purpose of sound social planning. The purpose is to simplify, to rationalize, to provide a stable set of alternatives in which individuals are freer to act in security and in the exercises of their freedom of choice."

It was writer Joseph Kraft, a participant at the Boston symposium on technology, who made most concrete and vivid the need for a new political superstructure if we are to manage the new technology. He made a plea reminiscent of Frankel's for new institutions to control and direct technological change, but on a grander scale than Frankel. The author of *The Grand Design: From Common Market to Atlantic Partnership,* Kraft spoke with enthusiasm of the "important political advance" represented by the European Economic Commission, on the one hand, and the Council of Ministers, on the other. The Commission consists of highly skilled technicians. The Council is a supranational body of ministers of state charged with making the political decisions of the European Economic Community. What has impressed Kraft about the Common Market is how its political framework enables it to adjust to technological change expeditiously and rationally. He cites the fact that, with the adoption of a common agricultural policy last January, the result in the next decade will be to move a million and a half inefficient West German farmers off the farm and into labor-short industry, as France's much more efficient farmers come to dominate Continental agriculture. His point is that this necessary and rational development would never have been possible if conventional German politics, with its powerful farm lobby, had prevailed. *What has happened, in effect, is that the technical experts of the European Economic Commission have become a permanent political lobby in favor of rational response to technological change.* The European Economic Commission is able to function so effectively because the Council of Ministers, being a supranational body, can then bring immense pressure to bear upon the individual governments to adopt the Commission's recommendations. For then the individual government, in this instance the West German government, says to the farmers, in Kraft's words, "Look, we understand your interests and are doing the best we can, but we don't have absolute control. There are these other people we have to consider."

Kraft sees the Commission and the Council as "an international system for diluting the responsibility of the individual governments" and thus enabling these national governments to go along with the reforms which conventional politics would otherwise have precluded. He sees the merging of the six Common Market powers as resulting, almost by accident, in a providential device for coping with technological change and feels that some such political device must be found by the United States if it is to overcome such standing blocks to progress as our inability to solve problems like subsidized farming, tax loopholes for industry, and featherbedding labor.

As a perceptive journalist, Kraft is impressed by how conventional political obstruction to needed technological adjustments has us currently immobilized in so many important areas. Herman Somers, the Haverford College political scientist, sharply questioned Kraft's evaluation of the Common Market experience. He contended that Kraft was saying nothing more than that parliamentary procedures were simply in temporary suspension when the Economic Commission's decisions were carried out and that as the Common Market countries evolved from an economic to a political unity the same "obstructionism" of parliamentary deliberation would again prevail. Neither he nor Kraft could then clarify how to escape the dilemma. Their colleague at the Boston symposium, economist and historian Robert Heilbroner (also prominent as a writer for the Arden House symposium), sees the impact of technology essentially as mortally challenging the traditional role of the market system as the organizer and arbiter of our political and social order.

In a prophetic concluding essay elaborating his viewpoint in his new book *The Making of Economic Society,* Heilbroner, like Gerard Piel at the Santa Barbara symposium and Bator at Brookings, sees the market mechanism as having "declining functional relevance" in a society of advanced technology: "The market is an assiduous servant of the wealthy consumer, but an indifferent servant to the poor one. Thus it presents us with the anomaly of a surplus of luxury housing existing side-by-side with a shortage of inexpensive housing, although the social need for the latter is incontestably greater than for the former. Or it pours energy and resources into the multiplication of luxuries for which the wealthier classes offer a market, while allowing more basic needs of the poor to go unheeded and unmet. . . . These shortcomings are all indicative of a central weakness of the market system—its inability to formulate public needs above those of the market place." Hence planning arises in the advanced market society which has mastered technology precisely to offset that society's inherent goal-setting weakness.

Technology further accentuates this goal-setting or planning deficiency of the market mechanism for two reasons. First, as Heilbroner puts it, "In a society of very great abundance, not only these cultivated desires but even the basic incentive to maximize income or minimize expenditures may well lose the ability to direct human behavior. (Who will clean the sewers and handle the garbage, for instance?) In that event the market system would cease to wield its necessary control over individual action, and society would have to look to some other means of social control to insure the necessary accomplishment of its basic tasks." It was apropos of this that RAND economist Charles Hitch at the Brookings symposium asserted, "If we don't have an adequate theory of efficiency in a non-market economy, and we certainly don't, it is high time we developed one." Hence the underlying theme of all the symposiums—the impending political crisis.

A recurrent note was that technology demands central planning because it presents a bewildering array of alternative actions and because it creates an enormously complex order in which all enterprises are interdependent, with each action exerting a chain reaction. A political superstructure capable of central planning becomes essential if only to prevent chaos. This is to express it defensively. The offensive was taken, as noted earlier, first at the Brookings symposium on economics, which served as a platform for suggestions that technological research and development be directly organized by the government so as to achieve planned socio-economic goals. At Santa Barbara the same note was sounded (and occasioned profound alarm) and the "declining functional relevance" of the market system was implicit throughout the discussions. There economist Robert Theobald quoted a Stanford Research Institute report to the United States Senate as follows: "We have invented the art of systematic invention. Organized scientific research and development, which has become a great industry in the last few decades, is itself one of the most significant social inventions of the twentieth century. It is unlocking the secrets of nature and putting the knowledge to practical use at an unprecedented rate. Also we have invented the art of systematic innovation."

The tremendous extent to which the United States is already devoting its treasure to technological advance under direct government auspices was recently shown in the testimony of Dr. Jerome Wiesner, the Director of the Office of Science and Technology, before the House Committee on Government Operations:

> This fiscal year the President proposes to put about $12.3 billion into research and development—more in one year than the Federal Government spent for research and development during the entire interval from the American Revolution through and including World War II. This $12.3 billion, although representing but 15 percent of the total Federal budget, is in effect well over one-third of that portion of the budget which is susceptible to control; for a great part of the budget, as we all know, is inevitably committed to fixed requirements such as debt retirement, etc. In addition, the Government now accounts for at least two-thirds of the Nation's entire annual expenditure in research. That is, the Federal Government spends twice as much for research and development as all of industry, universities and private foundations combined. This budget is not only large, but it has been growing at an unprecedented rate —for what in 1950 amounted to $1.2 billion has grown in the intervening 13 years by a factor of 10.

One great effect of this has been clearly explained by Professors J. S. Dupre and W. E. Gustafson of Harvard in a paper entitled "Contracting for Defense" (*Political Science Quarterly,* June 1962). "The government has had to devise new standards in its contractual relationships with business firms. Essentially, the government now assumes the financial risk involved in innovation. Free competition no longer characterizes the process of bidding for government contracts. While private firms have thus been freed from the restraints of the open market, they have acquired new public responsibilities. They are no longer merely suppliers to the government, but participants in the administration of public functions."

What is happening is that in the past companies competed on a bid basis in the open market for government contracts. Now, with immensely complicated projects whose evolution and ultimate costs can only be roughly surmised in advance, contracting firms negotiate agreements with the government to be reimbursed for costs. These firms are selected not on a price basis so much as on a basis of technical expertise, on their management calibre and their facilities. This is posing very delicate political issues with respect to conflict of interest. "Such public goals as cost control, the insurance of competition, and protection for small business all come into conflict with the profit motives," note Dupre and Gustafson. They point out that a prime contractor must take on management responsibilities in the public interest that are unnatural for a profit-seeking, competitive corporation. As prime contractor the firm has to make all kinds of judgments in acting as the overall coordinator. All the while it has to think of its own fortunes, for example in successfully competing for future contracts, and this accentuates its reluctance to make information available to participating contractors who may later be competitors.

Action has recently been taken by the executive branch responsive to precisely this situation in another instance of political decision following directly upon the admonitions of the academic community. In September the Defense Department announced that firms doing research-and-development work ("the lackeys of the death industry," as they were referred to at Santa Barbara) were to be barred from competing also for "hardware" contracts. This is a far-reaching decision because it puts at least a temporary halt upon the practice of non-profit corporations created by the government from intruding on the lucrative engineering and technical work of the established defense companies. This decision is the first to emerge from the analysis of the government's research and development program being undertaken by a committee headed by former Budget Director David E. Bell. The committee's underlying concern is the increasingly blurred dividing line between the economy's public and private sectors.

Dupre and Gustafson conclude that "business is no longer merely a supplier but a participant in the management and administration of a public function . . . negotiation and cost reimbursement have channeled public money into the private sector *without the use of the market mechanism. Business, like government, must then become subject to non-economic checks to avoid abuses.*" What non-economic checks is the precise question before the house, of course.

In his testimony to Congress pleading for more money to pay for scientists, Wiesner said that the step-up in government-subsidized research and development was bound to accelerate quite apart from defense or space work because it has now become clear that our rate of economic growth is increasingly dependent upon technological development. All the technology meetings noted the increased dependence of the economic growth rate on technological development. John T. Dunlop, the Harvard economist who edited the book on the Arden House symposium, said: "The industry of discovery opens up a new vista of the long future in which substantial resources in increasing amounts are devoted systematically to . . . reshaping the physical environment of mankind and to providing increased living standards and cultural opportunities . . . the rise of the industry of discovery suggests that we should be able to look forward to doubling productivity and living standards . . . every fifteen years (a rise from 3 to 5 percent in the yearly growth rate). These potentials underscore the common gains to be shared by increasing productivity and the possibilities of insuring adequately those who bear the costs of the adverse initial impacts of some technological changes. The industry of discovery also raises a host of issues and questions which are slowly coming to the fore. . . . *To what extent shall the direction of invention be left to the individual spirit and curiosity, to the market, and to what extent directed by priorities established by what bodies?"*

Thus the signs are accumulating that we are on the threshold of an increasingly hot and divisive national debate on this very question and that it may very well bring us to the brink of a constitutional crisis which cannot yet be precisely envisioned but will focus on the relations between the executive and legislative branches. It will be the central domestic issue of the 1960's and the 1970's. The manner in which the question is answered will determine our governmental framework for a generation, and especially the pattern of relationships between the national government and the other great power center, business, the administrator of the market system.

How distant, really, is the time when, as Robert Theobald stressed at Santa Barbara, the issues of biological and genetic control will be forced upon the agenda of government responsibilities under such prods as the population explosion of the senile and chronically ill, the possibilities of organ transplants, new miracle drugs and artificial insemination? Professor Somers cites the work of the British physician Ffrangcon Roberts, an expert on medical economics, who uses the wry term "medicated survival" to describe technology's accomplishments in forestalling death. He sees the market system as nourishing "antiplutic medicine," that is, treatment wherein society remains burdened despite treatment because the disease is congenital or the result of old age—"antiplutic" since the very success of the treatment exacerbates the cost to society. But the examples need hardly be so esoteric. The pressures are mounting behind such familiar questions (forcefully raised at Boston) as whether a decentralized democracy traditionally infatuated with "local initiative" can cope with automotive congestion, originating across different state and city boundaries; or whether, as open land in metropolitan areas shrinks, we can devise institutions to prevent corrupting land uses; or whether the potential of television, now about to become international, is indefinitely to be determined by its effectiveness as a sales instrument for advertisers.

As the inadequacies of the market system become increasingly evident under the impact of technological change, there is a developing consensus that we are bound to witness a kind of intervention now feared by most Americans. Practically the only precedent we have for it is the Employment Act of 1946, which for the first time in Federal law stipulated that full employment and equitable income distribution were to become an explicit governmental concern rather than be left up to the market system. That law was passed in response to the national anxiety that the economy would falter with the end of wartime spending. (As it turned out, massive pent-up consumer demand more than compensated.) It was no radical dismissal of our system, but rather an acknowledgement that, in an age of technological disruption, supplementation of the market system by political action is essential for rational allocation of resources and the meeting of public needs. This year's Manpower Development and Training Act is the most important addition to the law so far.

Almost certainly we are also going to witness the development of a new kind of national economic budget going beyond annual Federal accounting (what we essentially do now) to set forth a five or six year projection of all our national resources viewed against our national goals. We will then have something close to national programming of explicit policies, in which the overriding consideration will be the role of new technology.

Just what government body will emerge as the key agency for national planning no one could say now. But it could conceivably be the President's Council of Economic Advisers, a Council further strengthened by law and with vastly increased responsibilities and powers. It is such a body that must to a substantial extent fulfill the crucial function the European Economic Commission fulfills for the Common Market. One of the best prescriptions for such an agency as this is developed in the extraordinarily penetrating statement on automation issued by the Research Section of the Industrial Union Department, AFL-CIO. It calls for "A Permanent Commission on Technological Change" to act as "a central clearing house in which there will be gathered, analyzed, and evaluated, all pertinent information on public and private plans involving technological change." It would operate within the executive branch of the national government. Recently Arthur Burns, the former economic adviser to President Eisenhower, came forward with a surprisingly similar proposal.

The development of any such planning body and such a new kind of national economic budget to cope with technological change will no doubt create and be part of a great political ferment. But by then the domestic political context may also have been modified somewhat to ease the impact. For example, in the years immediately ahead we can anticipate some modernization of the organization of Congress. As the reapportionment movement slowly eliminates the most egregious abuses and begins to alter the complexion of our government, it may in time modify the American custom of putting local interests ahead of the national interest.

We will also witness the growing power of a new constituency in the electorate, a constituency created by technology itself. I refer to the burgeoning army of scientists and other intellectual workers of the new technological order. If Professor Daniel Bell of Columbia, a participant at the Boston symposium on technology where he first unveiled his now much-discussed vision of the "post-industrial society," is correct—and his statistically-awesome arguments were compelling—this new constituency will soon come to rival the dominant voice of the past, the business community. The rise of this constituency could be the most important single political development of the new technology. Dr. James R. Killian, Jr., Wiesner's predecessor as Presidential science adviser, has urged that scientists run for Congress. Noting that they have begun to appear in state legislatures, Killian suggested that a technological society must have scientists "in the public arena if it is to deal wisely with all the great policy matters arising out of science and technology."

In any event, one thing is clearer day by day. The American instinct for freedom, the talent of political inventiveness permitting a maximum of individual freedom combined with optimum collective performance, is to be put to a rugged test. To meet the test we will have to arrive at a far better comprehension of the full impact of technology. With planning to a much larger extent superseding the market mechanism as the director of our energies, there is bound to be much more discussion as to what worthy ends our political and social institutions should serve. There will be a growing consciousness that, as Robert Oppenheimer recently elaborated in his piece on science and culture in *Encounter*, whereas technology is a cumulative process ever building on its advances and thus moves only in the direction of progress, our moral and political life lacks cumulative growth and can at any time just as easily regress as progress. As of right now Americans are still floundering in a strange transitional state of mind, for the most part blindly addicted to the notion that the old market system will make everything come out all right; the rest uneasily awakening to the realization that only our resilience as a free people will see us through the crisis.